WARD H

An Adventure in Innovation

by

NICK J. COLARELLI
St. Louis University

and

SAUL M. SIEGEL
Ohio State University

AN INSIGHT BOOK

D. VAN NOSTRAND COMPANY, INC.

PRINCETON, NEW JERSEY

TORONTO   LONDON

NEW YORK

Dedicated
to
the memory of
ESTHER MARTHA WATTS
with respect and affection

D. VAN NOSTRAND COMPANY, INC.
120 Alexander St., Princeton, New Jersey
(*Principal Office*)
24 West 40 Street, New York 18, New York

D. VAN NOSTRAND COMPANY, LTD.
358, Kensington High Street, London, W.14, England

D. VAN NOSTRAND COMPANY (Canada), LTD.
25 Hollinger Road, Toronto 16, Canada

Published simultaneously in Canada by
D. VAN NOSTRAND COMPANY (Canada), LTD.

Preface

To those who took part in it, the Ward H project was an adventure—an adventure whose story the authors hope to tell in this book. As the project elicited involvement and commitment from every participant, it had a marked personal impact; and as each member of the research team benefited from and built upon his need for the others, the experiment became an immensely gratifying group enterprise. But it is difficult to convey this side of the story. Only the skilled dramatist could compellingly and accurately tell of the truly human experience of personal growth, pain, triumph, and challenge. The authors, however, are not dramatists; to help overcome the frustrations encountered in describing the Ward H adventure, we offer this introduction as a program to the play. Through it we wish to sensitize the reader to the story's most significant aspects.

The setting can be found in almost any large organization, where man frequently experiences himself as a cog in a huge impersonal machine over which he has little control and in which he finds little opportunity to realize either his uniqueness or his commonness.

Perhaps this situation is most sharply demonstrated in what Erving Goffman, in his work *Asylums*, has called "total institutions." These institutions, such as monasteries, the armed services, and mental hospitals, provide total care for their "inmates." To some extent the inmates' "raison d'être" is to provide an opportunity for someone else to care for them. His need to be protected, fed, and cared for gives institutional man his value. It is only natural that in such an institution the inmate's humanness increasingly diminishes. Who he is, what he is, his individual hopes, problems, and concerns recede into the background; he becomes an object—an object who fits into a routine, a bureaucratic pattern—to be cared for like any other object. As long as he remains in this role of the cared-for object, and as long as the institution's staff members are willing to be caretakers, the cogs of the machine mesh and the intricate balance is maintained. The machine grinds on. Life, time, space, and human experience become undifferentiated.

Within recent years impressive strides have been made in combating the dehumanization of the mental patient. Perhaps nowhere has the effort to humanize the treatment of the mentally ill been more dramatic than at Topeka State Hospital. In 1948, with the backing of an aroused public and an informed legislature, and under the guidance of the Menninger Foundation, a revolt against dehumanization took place. The story has been told many times elsewhere. The Ward H project is in many ways a part of that revolt and could not have happened without it. But this adventure occurred ten years later and with another kind of patient, the patient known as the "chronic schizophrenic"; he is a patient who has been hospitalized for many years and has proved intractable to most other forms of treatment; who, despite the best intentions and the best efforts of an enlightened staff, loses his humanity, possibly because it was never well developed to begin with. It is difficult to regard him as a person—and yet he fills a majority of the beds in our mental hospitals. We have known little about him and his treatment until recent times. He is the main character in our story.

However, we have a protagonist too. The mainstay of any mental hospital is found in its psychiatric aides. They have been the eyes, ears, and hands of the doctor; they have acted as middlemen between patient and doctor. Their presence has permitted one doctor to treat many patients. They have reported faithfully their observation of the patient and have carried out prescriptions and treatment. Because they have served this function so well, for most patients the mental hospital has become a place of hope. But not for the chronic patient. For him, whose personality is so devastated, this system has defects. For him, the aide, as helper to the doctor, is not a model for treatment, but for humane custodial care.

These then are the characters in our story: the patient, the aides, and the professional staff.

The story has a plot. The issue is, "How do you change the static hopelessness of these patients?" How does one humanize them and their treatment? How does one relate to them as persons? How stop the process of dull, un-

ending routinization of the personality? A possibility is to
provide them with a model—someone lively, fully human,
spirited; someone who cries, laughs, struggles with life.
Let us put this person near them. Perhaps through identification, through learning, the patient will come alive.

Who will serve as our model? Let's put the aide in this
role. We see our aides at parties and in their personal
lives and know that they are spirited and vital. Why
aren't they their own vigorous selves at the hospital?

It is hard for them to be themselves. They are middlemen; their function is to be an extension of the doctor.
But while this arrangement works for many patients, it
doesn't seem to work for these lost ones. So instead of
making the aides middlemen, let us make them headmen.
Let us give them patients and tell them that they are
totally responsible for those patients and their treatment.
If the aides want help from the staff they can ask for it,
but the treatment is up to them and we confidently expect results.

The aides will have something to struggle over—their
own patients. Whether they make mistakes or not, let us
trust them and encourage them to be themselves, to find
out what they are. Let them make their own mistakes;
their pain will be their own, but so will their triumph. If
we can do that, we will have our model.

Yes, but how do we do it? Why not apply the same
logic as before? If a model will help the patients, perhaps
a model will help the aides. Why don't we relate to the
aides in the same way that we want them to relate to the
patients? Why don't we struggle with them, make them
our problem, commit ourselves to them? Maybe they will
learn to do the same with their patients.

So far, that is the plot. How does the story develop?
What becomes manifest first is the humanity of the aides;
and in time we begin to see the humanity of the patients.
But this play also had an audience, and, while the actors
were on Ward H, the audience was the rest of the staff.

Many of the nonparticipating staff were not simply
passive observers. Often they were also called onto the
stage of Ward H. They usually found their role challenging because it was so different from that of the rest of the
hospital. They became involved, but expected the plot to
develop in another way. Frequently these staff members

were conditioned by previous experiences and investments to see the aides in their conventional character rather than in the new one required by our experiment. It became evident that at times the play was neither entertaining nor stimulating to the audience. They wondered why they had spent their money, or wanted to ask for a rain check. Why? This was a good audience. They had seen many stories unfold; they had initiated and participated in numerous adventures.

What made this play so difficult to watch? Some said they thought the story was not valid because the patient and his problems were not perceived accurately; consequently they thought the whole plot faulty. Others were concerned about the protagonist; they had a lot of respect for the aides, but wondered whether the role was not over their heads. After all, the aides had no credentials from a respectable school of acting. Some thought that although the story was valid the plot seemed unnecessarily different; it forced the audience into an unfamiliar pattern of thinking. What was the matter with the old ways of telling stories, of writing and presenting plays? And finally, some said that the play was too challenging, that it asked too much of the audience, and that these demands were unrealistic; an audience has certain expectations and will be dissatisfied if they are not met. Further, said some critics, not all would find this story of interest or would wish to share in it.

As the characters of the story and the audience continued their dialogue, the story changed. It became apparent that both characters and audience were part of a larger unity, Topeka State Hospital. They became more and more aware of their interdependence.

These, then, are our program notes. We hope they will be of service to our reader without unduly restricting his own experience of the story.

NICK. J. COLARELLI
SAUL M. SIEGEL

Acknowledgments

The work to be described in this book represents the collective ideas, influences, and commitments of many people. The project was not designed by the authors and carried out with the assistance of others. Instead, the many people involved in the program were asked to participate in it in a way that would influence its evolvement. As each member entered into the project and as each grew with it, he added new dimensions to the project itself. What we should like to acknowledge, then, is not just the assistance of the following people, but rather their active presence and participation, their commitment, their willingness to look for themselves within the framework of the project. Without them, the results would have taken a different form, and in this sense, it is their project.

Because there is far too little space here for adequate expression of the appreciation we owe so many, we have attempted to list those to whom we are indebted in an order that roughly represents chronological association with the project. For many and diverse special reasons, we sincerely thank the following: Alfred Paul Bay, Superintendent of Topeka State Hospital; Austin Des Lauriers, who formulated the basic theory for the treatment of schizophrenics used in this work; Samuel Buker, whose encouragement led us to seek the financial support of the National Institute of Mental Health and broaden the scope of our investigations with the aid of project grant MH-770; Suzanne Reyes, Richard Meadows, Etta Williams, Lois Martin, Gordon Warme, Mary Jackson, Marcia Becker, Genitha Clark, Lugene Burton, Arthur Herman, Thomas McNaught, Charles Chediak, Teodoro Braganza, Mary Patton, Barbara Cavallin, Christine Nagel, Thelma Long; Esther Watts, Beatrice Jones, Beverly Walsh, Corrine Nelson, Irma Stillman, Beverly Taylor, Helen Lewis, Mary Ross, Theodosia Douglas, Barbara Hale, Mary Lampkins; William Key of Washburn University, Robert Blake and Jane Mouton of the University of Texas, Edward Wike of Kansas University, John Overall of Kansas State University, Donald Leventhal of Washburn University, Donald Saidel; Elizabeth Novotny, Rosaline Finestein, Barbara Saidel, William Svoboda, William Griffith; Betty Collier; Mary Donahue; Helen Friend, and Jane Smith. A special note of appreciation must be expressed for the tolerance and cooperation given by the general administrative staff and department heads of the hospital.

We would like to thank our wives, who tolerated our preoccupation, our late hours and unpredictable interruptions in family life, and who sympathetically endured the project's moments of crisis.

Finally, we would like to acknowledge the participation of the patients who lived on Ward H. It was they who provided the challenge and it was their response to the aides' efforts that created the enthusiasm and vitality that was so much a part of this project.   N. J. C.

S. M. S.

Contents

I

The Hospital

The setting for this project, the hospital, like an individual, must be understood in terms of its history, its community, its physical and intellectual equipment, and the major influences, especially people, in its life.

PHYSICAL AND STAFF FACILITIES

The hospital is organized into six units: the Kansas Treatment Center for Children, with preadolescent and adolescent wings; the Adult Out-Patient Clinic; and four adult in-patient treatment sections.

The architectural style of the hospital is hybrid: cupcake cupolas ornamented the main building for many years; stone exteriors, wood and stucco interiors down long dayhall corridors with high-arched, narrow windows still characterize the wards of older buildings. This kind of structure was originally designed by Dr. Thomas Kirkbride and is found in many state hospital buildings in this country. At this institution the dayhall is 156 by 13 feet with short halls and rooms adjoining for sleeping dormitories, allowing for two to eight beds, nursing stations, and the dining room for the patients. Modern buildings are slowly replacing the outmoded buildings. These new buildings reflect changes in treatment philosophy and provide the structure for the new programs that progressively change the work of the hospital.

The grounds are spacious and lovely, invariably green and inviting, even in the frequently blazing Kansas summer sun. Besides the hospital's treatment facilities, the ninety acres they cover also contain the houses of six of the hospital's administrators, buildings of an institute for the blind, and a testing bureau of the State Department of Agriculture. There is also a ball diamond

1

which is used as a home field for Little League clubs; around the diamond by six o'clock on summer evenings there are clusters of parents and patients watching Johnny practice for the big game.

Each adult treatment section is staffed by a psychiatrist as a section chief; two assistant section chiefs who are also psychiatrists; four to six resident psychiatrists; a section nurse; two psychologists; three social workers, one of whom supervises all social work on the section; four or five adjunctive therapists, one of whom also is in charge of the section's adjunctive therapy activities; five nurses; and approximately seventy-five to eighty aides. Each section is divided into five to seven wards and houses 250 patients.

ORGANIZATIONAL STRUCTURE

As is traditional in state hospitals, Topeka State Hospital is organized so that most employees serve two masters. The personnel of each section are responsible to the section chief for carrying out the section's overall treatment program and its goals. It is not possible, however, for the section chief to be aware of, or competent to supervise and evaluate, the work of persons from professional disciplines different from his own. Thus, for the level, techniques, and competence of their functioning, personnel are responsible to their respective department heads, who in turn form a part of the central administrative group of the hospital. A social worker, for example, works closely with a clinical team in relation to decisions made about particular patients, while the head of the department of social work supervises her professional work and rates her competence. Potential difficulties are clearly evident, such as the possible division of loyalties of the employee and the lack of a clear demarcation where a section chief's responsibility ends and a department head's begins; smooth working relationships and a good communication system between the staff members are essential to solve these problems.

The organization as it relates to patient treatment involves the delegation of responsibility from the section chief to the ward physician, who oversees the course of the patient's hospitalization. It is the ward physician, aided by the suggestions of the ward team, which includes those aides, nurses, psychologists, and social workers concerned with the case, who prescribes appropriate treatment. It is the nurse's responsibility to see that these prescriptions are carried out. Much of the "carrying out" is done by the aides.

There are several aspects to Topeka State Hospital that are of particular relevance to the project under discussion that should be mentioned here. First and foremost, Topeka State Hospital is a training institution for virtually all of the clinical professions represented on the staff. Physicians training to become psychiatrists provide much of the psychiatric team leadership within the institution. The psychiatric residents attend lectures in the Menninger School of Psychiatry, which integrates theory and its practical use in the daily treatment of patients.

In recent years many of the psychiatric residents who have come to Topeka State Hospital for training have been citizens of foreign countries and received their medical training there. Most of these physicians come with few preconceived ideas of how an American hospital *should* function and therefore are frequently more open to innovation.

One consequence of the residency training program is a regularly scheduled change of residents on a ward every six, nine, or twelve months. As in every hospital, above all the psychiatric hospital, changes in assignment are essential for a well-rounded training program. Many patients, especially the acute and newly admitted ones, benefit from these changes in personnel, where new ideas and personalities are constantly focused on problems and the ever-changing environment generated makes lapsing into a chronic role difficult. One negative aspect of this changing environment, however, is the frequent disruption of the therapeutic relationship built up between the patient and the resident, often resulting in a setback or regression in the patient's recovery. A patient suffering a regression every six months as a result of the rotation of the ward physician may learn to resist therapy by avoiding deep personal relationships with the physician. The disadvantages of this program for the proposed treatment of chronic schizophrenic patients will be discussed in a later chapter.

Another relevant aspect of the institution is the high caliber of its nursing aides. Part of the reason for the aides' superior quality is the population from which they are drawn. Topeka is not an industrial city, and for the sizable Negro, Indian, and Mexican communities there, work as an aide at Topeka State Hospital is a comparatively well-paying, high-status position. Consequently, competition for these positions is high and the aide group is a relatively well-educated, intelligent segment of the local population. Unlike state hospitals that are located in rural areas, this group of employees at Topeka State Hospital has had many of the varied and sophisticated experiences common to urban living, without the provincialism which often characterizes those drawn from exclusively rural environments. But because Topeka is not an industrial city and the employment situation is fairly stable, the hospital does not have the problem of transiency among aides common to many urban centers.[1]

Topeka State has a highly developed training program for its psychiatric aides, initiated in 1950 by a grant from the Ford Foundation implemented by Dr. Bernard Hall and his associates. During the first three months of their employment, aides attend classes, learn how to take blood pressure readings, how to control an unmanageable patient, how to deal with the various categories of psychiatric illness and the most common behavioral manifestations of these illnesses. Hospital policies and procedures and the normal chain of command are also a part of this training. After this phase of their training is complete, the aides are sent to a training area on a ward for six months before being permanently assigned to a specific ward.

CLIMATE FOR INNOVATION

At many state mental institutions status-quo is the hallmark, and even minor innovations become matters of overwhelming concern and anxiety. New medical

[1] Such transiency is described by M. M. Hunt in "Profiles: Pilgrim State Hospital." *The New Yorker*, Vol. 37, pp. 51ff. Sept. 30, 1961.

procedures are frequently difficult to introduce, and those that relate to changes in organization or employee functioning are especially difficult. The climate at Topeka State Hospital is more receptive to innovation, however, than at many similar institutions. The aspects of this climate that will be discussed here, including those that may limit innovation, are those that are particularly relevant to this study.

The hospital has a strong research department which has been responsible for a number of projects. Among its more recent investigations was a two-year study of the usefulness of social work aides as replacements for social workers in certain activities. One project, known as "the saturation study," was designed to investigate the effect of having two or three times the minimum number of aides in a ward as specified by the American Psychiatric Association. In another project, the hospital has begun a series of studies on the effects of architecture on behavior in conjunction with the Department of Architecture at the University of Kansas. One of these studies is aimed at developing inexpensive ways of remodeling the old Kirkbride buildings still in use in many state hospitals for newer treatment approaches; another is an attempt to describe the change in social structure that occurs when patients move from old to modern buildings.

The administrative philosophy of the institution is characterized by faith in the capacity of each staff member to grow and a desire to provide each with adequate freedom and opportunities. Members of the staff are held accountable for their own areas of responsibility, but there is little keyhole supervision. This philosophy was reflected by the hospital's superintendent, Dr. Alfred Bay, in an address given to the National Association for Mental Health:

> . . . What we found out a long time ago about patient behavior is equally valid for most other individuals; that is, they have a way of living up to our expectations of them. . . . Startling progress could be made if more men were given the opportunity to do the things they wanted to do in a way they want to do them and were held accountable, not for methods, but for results.[2]

[2] Alfred Paul Bay, M.D., "A Time for Action," *Mental Hygiene*, Vol. 47, No. 2, p. 193.

As a deliberate policy there are few explicit norms and many exceptions. The organizational goals to which commitment is a requirement are few. There is as a result a creative atmosphere which fosters the feeling of responsibility and a desire to think constructively. Most of the clinical staff operate in a responsible yet free-wheeling fashion; initiative and personal style are permitted or encouraged, although, as in most institutions, a certain number of antique organizational rules still persist.

There are external forces that serve as limitations to change and innovation in the hospital, and these inhibiting circumstances also form a part of the overall climate. There are the usual problems faced by any public institution. Unlike private institutions, the hospital is subject to scrutiny and questioning by any official or citizen and may easily become the source of subtle pressures. Under such circumstances, the administration's talent for keeping the staff free enough to be creative is very important. Again, this point has been made by the superintendent:

> . . . The organization, moreover, never exists in a vacuum. In the case of a public agency its purposes are inextricably bound up with the purposes of many other agencies and individuals—purchasing agents, personnel divisions, budget bureaus, legislators, governors, board of control and the public.[3]

In common with most state hospitals, another pressure is the public demand for more services than the budget and facilities permit. For example, the demand for treatment of delinquent adolescents forces administrators to send adolescents to the less crowded but understaffed adult wards. Here the still immature fifteen-year-old may feel at a disadvantage since he is no longer with his own age group but with men or women of all ages. He reacts by demanding more staff time. Situations such as this may force the ward staff to make choices as to which patients will be most actively treated. Generally when faced with such a choice the staff will give most active treatment to the younger patient who shows the best possibility of responding. This involuntary favoritism in turn leads to secondary iatrogenic symptoms for the

[3] Bay, "A Time for Action," p. 191.

other patients, creating a situation where, if it continues unabated, these patients may become chronic.

Unfortunately, most citizens with hospitalized relatives are not aware of these pressures which burden the staff, waste their time, and dissipate the energies better devoted to treatment. Relatives' primary interest is, of course, with the treatment and improvement of their particular family member or friend.

Among the internal forces that form a part of the institution's climate and may inhibit the introduction of innovation, one of the most important is the noticeable efforts by the members of the various disciplines to exaggerate their professionalism either to distinguish themselves from other groups or to establish a professional identity. Hence, for example, the attitudes fostered during professional training lead the professional at times to make much of differences between therapy, counseling, casework, and "tender loving care," rather than to emphasize the common aspects of these "helping professions." This concentration on fraternity or sect membership rather than individual worth is frequently found and tolerated in the community at large. Such an attitude is discrepant with the therapeutic premise that humans are not radically different from one another.

Another important internal factor in the organization of the hospital is that the therapeutic orientation has, since the revolution of 1950, become fairly fixed. Understanding, particularly self-knowledge, is one of the principal values characteristic of this orientation. Partly because of the training orientations of the psychiatrists, psychologists, and residents on the staff, a premium is placed upon understanding of the patient's problem in psychoanalytic terms. The patient is regarded as showing signs of "improvement" when he expresses interest in and understanding of his problems. The emphasis is upon self-knowledge as a vehicle for mastering reality rather than upon guided, direct experience. The treatment program frequently stresses understanding the patient's problem rather than active intervention in the patient's handling of it.

Another factor is essentially social in nature. In general, the normative values of those in the mental health professions are drawn from the middle class. Behavior by the patient which deviates from the norms of middle-class values tends, therefore, to be labeled as pathologic. A patient's attitudes toward ownership, indebtedness, credit, education, self-improvement, and hard work can be described as "pleasure-oriented" or "narcissistic"; his inability to talk about his problem, "resistance"; his unwillingness to act on his problems, "passive aggression"; his drunken binge may be regarded as "acting out his impulses"; his resorting to fighting or physical attacks upon his wife may be labeled "lack of adequate symbolic development"; and a female patient's sexual behavior may be called "promiscuous" or "deviant."

A final internal force to be mentioned is the fact that Topeka State Hospital is a *hospital* and the medical structure is difficult to change. The hierarchical system which is taught in medical schools to doctors and their associated professionals was created to serve certain specific needs which to some extent exist in all hospitals. This whole system has become incorporated into many of the laws governing hospitals. Because of this legalistic rigidity those innovations which are inconsistent with this structure have less chance of becoming a permanent part of hospital routine.

2

The Problem of the Chronic Patients

In Chapter 1 we have discussed the hospital as a service agency. The patient population comes from the 36 northeastern counties of the state and is admitted by a variety of procedures. Some are sent by the courts for observation, others come voluntarily. The latter group has become an increasing proportion in the past few years. In the years preceding the present era, ending about 1950, the population was very stable, and to the group of about 1,800, only 150 were admitted per year. Average length of stay was measured in years; the bulk of the population was seen as chronic. After an exposé of conditions, this situation changed radically in the early 1950's; and with progressive political leadership and professional guidance a great transformation took place.

About half the present population of about 1,000 could be called chronic, having been in the institution for more than one year. For the balance the stay is short, averaging 60 days. The overall diagnostic categories of patients have not changed; the majority are psychotic, mostly schizophrenics, but there are also persons with depressions, severe neurotic problems, and character problems. Some patients are able to leave their wards on weekend passes, others spend only their nights at the hospital, still others spend only daytime hours there.

Over the years it has become apparent that the insitution has operated two concurrent treatment programs. The first concerns the acutely disturbed patient who in his more recent past has demonstrated the capability for both personal and social responsibility. These patients are generally characterized by short-term hospitalization, a good response to "talking" therapy, rapid and at times dramatic recovery from disabling symptoms, infrequent readmissions, and a resourceful family that makes important contributions to the patient's recovery.

The other program concerns the "chronic" patient.

Unlike the acute patients, these generally undergo long periods of hospitalization. If discharged, the probability of their readmission is quite high. The families of such chronic patients have few resources to offer in the recovery process. The patients themselves seldom respond to "talking" therapy, and consequently in their treatment there is a heavy reliance upon the use of tranquilizers and highly organized activity programs. For a significant proportion of these patients the goal of the hospital is placement in a protected environment such as a nursing home once their more socially inappropriate symptoms have subsided.

While the hospital has had a great deal of success in the treatment of the acute patient, it has been less proud of its achievements with the chronic. In part this failure has been a product of the pressures mentioned above which have not permitted the hospital to allocate adequate resources to treatment of the chronically ill. However, this is not the full story. There were indications that current treatment programs were not as effective as might be desired with this group.

The total patient census at Topeka State Hospital had dropped from 1,800 in 1948 to less than 1,000 in 1960. During the same decade the hospital's admission rate quadrupled. That methods of treatment were effective principally in cases of acutely ill patients is reflected in these trends. From 1953 to 1960 the hard core of chronic patients decreased from 1,100 to 600; but there was evidence that these patients were becoming less responsive to current methods of treatment. A formal assessment of the unresponsive group indicated that it was becoming an increasingly pure culture of chronic schizophrenic patients.

As a consequence, these patients had become an increasingly difficult group to work with. In many ways they are like very young children, but show little of the startlingly quick growth of children. Progress is so slow as to be almost imperceptible. Regression is frequent.

To characterize this "pure" group by generalities is inaccurate but does hold some validity. The chronic patients have an impaired sense of time; their memories may be quite lucid, especially of many things which happened years ago. They can recapture thoughts, actions, and sometimes even feelings while having no conception of how long ago these events occurred. A patient may tell about an event, discuss it animatedly for an hour, then disclose that it took place many years ago. There is a lack of sense of relevance; for example, he may communicate in the same breath and with the same level of intensity that he stubbed his toe, his mother died, and the trees were green. But most striking is the absence of appropriate affect or emotion; conversing with a chronic schizophrenic is often like talking to a machine. The normal individual usually responds both emotionally and intellectually to any event. In contrast, the chronic schizophrenic patient seems to have no understandable emotional response to an event.

When the chronic schizophrenic does react, it is usually in the same way whatever the situation. He may employ only one pattern of response whether he is sad, angry, lonely, or happy. The feeling inside may not be inappropriate to the occasion, but the ordinary channels of communication do not function and he knows only one way of expressing emotion. Sometimes there is a time lapse between his internal response and the visible motoric expression of the emotion.

Patients of this type may have trouble associating cause and effect in their own persons and bodies because they do not realize the boundaries of their bodies, any more than the boundaries of their minds. For example, one patient was quite disturbed and hostile, hitting out at everyone and everything. Her physical discomfort came from a very large blister on her heel; apparently to her, however, it seemed that the universe was making her uncomfortable. Only after an aide repeatedly manipulated the shoe which caused the blister, pressed on the blister, and then applied salve to the hurt heel was the patient able to understand that this pain was not general and the result of a malignant world but very specific and localized, the result of a badly fitting high-heeled shoe.

Characteristically, these people are disturbed by delusions and hallucinations which they may suffer in silence or act upon as though real. This latter reaction appears to be related to the intensity of the feelings generated within the schizophrenics and their inability to separate feelings from very real and exaggerated physical reactions.

Most staff members are discouraged by the lack of response from these patients and the difficulty of making contact with them. The psychiatric aides who work with these patients are chiefly responsible for their personal safety and physical welfare and for maintaining the security of the ward. These responsibilities demand most of the aides' time and energy. To see that the patients are regularly fed, clothed, and do not escape or harm one another takes considerable patience and effort. There is little time left to attend to the problems of the individual patient in any therapeutic sense. The drain of the physical demands upon the staff leaves little motivation for a therapeutic attitude. Needless to say, hope for improvement becomes difficult to maintain. Life on such a ward takes on a terrifying anonymity.

Developing more effective methods of treatment for this increasingly "pure" culture has long been a vital concern of the hospital. One of the most promising efforts was that of Austin DesLauriers.[1] While chief psychologist at Topeka State Hospital during the early 1950's, Dr. DesLauriers had developed a treatment theory from his work with chronic and childhood schizophrenics.

In brief, this theory held that schizophrenia was indicative of a step missed in the maturation of an infant—the step in which he learns the boundaries of his body and then of his ego.[2] Although at the time there may be nothing apparently wrong with the child's behavior, although he may appear to develop normally, in later life this lack of definition of ego boundaries catches up with him.

Rather than focusing upon those aspects of schiz-

---

[1] Austin DesLauriers, "The Psychological Experience of Reality in Schizophrenia," *Theoretical Implications in Chronic Schizophrenia*, ed. Appleby, Scheer and Cummings, Free Press, 1960.

[2] The "ego" is meant to define a hierarchy of successively more complex, highly differentiated, and tightly integrated organizations of experience that provide for the personality a capacity to act, synthesize experience and adapt to reality in a meaningful and gratifying manner.

ophrenia which are indicative of a regression in the face of stress to less adequate forms of behavior, this approach focuses upon schizophrenia as a matter of retardation, stunted growth, and an incomplete personality structure. Schizophrenia, then, was defined as a structural deficiency of personality which prevents the possibility of experiencing reality and relationships. Therefore, the process of recovery is dependent on reinstating those conditions necessary for experiencing reality and relationships.

Certainly this is only one of many theories of schizophrenia, each having demonstrable usefulness under certain conditions. To some, this particular approach showed promise for working with this "pure" culture of schizophrenics under the prevailing conditions at Topeka State Hospital.

Since in this system schizophrenia is not seen as a purposive retreat from the world but rather as a breaking down of the mechanisms for reaching out, the therapy consists of building a relationship. Since body boundaries are not defined, there must be physical contact and motion to reestablish these. It is the contact with another person which is important; and it must be a whole person involved with the whole patient, rather than simply a "therapist."

Essentially the problem is being present and constructing a relationship with the patient. To do this, one must be intrusive, a model for the individual, a helper but also someone who requires the patient to grow and eventually assume increasing responsibility. From this point of view all initiative rests with the worker, since he cannot expect the patient to initiate contact with him—he must assume the patient cannot.

The treatment theory presumes a loss of ego feeling in the schizophrenic. The individual is unable in any stable and constant way to experience himself as real and as differentiated from what is not himself. Therefore the treatment effort is directed at bringing about in the patient a structural change whereby his responses,

instead of being undifferentiated and aimless, can become specialized, goal-directed and reality-bound. To do this, the therapist must establish himself as the most important intruding factor in the life of the schizophrenic. This is not

14 WARD H: AN ADVENTURE IN INNOVATION

a question of "rapport," of transference, or of a warm positive relationship; it is taken for granted by the therapist that no meaningful relationship is possible between the patient and himself, and that his effort will be to create conditions whereby such a relationship can eventually become possible. If it is not a question of relationship with the patient, what is it then? It is a matter of *presence*; a forceful, insistent, intruding presence of the therapist to the patient, so that the schizophrenic cannot escape this presence. All the energies of the therapist must be geared to establishing, maintaining or encouraging, and developing "contact" between the patient and himself. The word "contact" is used here in its broadest sense; it includes physical, sensual, intellectual, affective, emotional, conative, and motoric contact between the patient and the therapist. A patient may not talk, but when you hold his hand he returns the pressure. He has, in one way, indicated that he knows you are there and he knows he is there. Communication then between the patient and the therapist becomes the equivalent of contact as defined here.[3]

The authors had had experience in the use of this theory and its effectiveness when applied by individual staff members to individual patients. Their major concern, however, was the practical problem of utilizing what appeared to be a promising approach in terms of the resources available to the hospital.

Implied in this approach are several requirements which should characterize the people who work with schizophrenics, especially those whose illness is chronic. The workers must be ever-present. They must be responsible people so they can serve as models. They must be sufficiently forceful to foster growing independence in the patients, but flexible, warm, and accepting enough to tolerate frequent regression and endless repetition. They must be comfortable working with the patients in concrete terms, since concrete reality must be firmly fixed before abstractions can be developed.

Who, of the staff available in the usual psychiatric hospital, would best fit these needs? The ward doctor does not have sufficient time to spend more than a few

[3]Austin DesLauriers, *The Experience of Reality in Childhood Schizophrenia*. New York: International Universities Press, Inc. 1962, pp. 62-63.

hours a week with each patient. As a therapist he has been trained at great expense and trouble to help people achieve insights into their problems. Could it possibly be profitable or practical to take him from a work he does well to expend great efforts on something for which his education, in all likelihood, makes him uncomfortable?

The nurse occupies the middle role in the psychiatric hospital. Historically the nursing profession has been conservative, the preserver of tradition. The education of the psychiatric nurse is aimed toward many of the same ends as that of the psychiatrist, though it is less intense and in many ways more pragmatic. Still, nursing is a profession which has cherished rules rather than innovation. And there are almost as few psychiatric nurses available as psychiatrists.

A remaining possibility is the psychiatric aide. "Certainly," the professional staff member would say, "the aide is an important member of the ward team." But he —and many others—may distrust the aide's competence and feel he requires constant supervision. However, the aides are there, lots of them, all the time. They are capable of communicating in concrete, nonverbal terms. They can be warm and spontaneous. They usually do not mind doing things over and over. And they are more than eager to work for innovations which might relate them more closely to the professional staff. They also welcome a chance to become invested in the patients under their care since previously emotional investment was often either impossible or forbidden. In addition, in their private lives the aides, like the professional staff, daily demonstrate their capacity for personal and social responsibility. Frequently, because the aides have spent more of their formative years in the "real" world rather than in the "ivory tower" of the university, they are more socially mature than many of the professional staff.

THE PILOT PROJECT

To explore the practical applications of this approach to the ward, one of the authors who was a staff psychologist on Stone Section, began in 1959 a one-year project for intrusive treatment of chronic schizophrenics. He had become interested in this idea after presenting several cases during consultation sessions with Dr. DesLauriers.

When he had examined the records of the chronic schizophrenic women on Ward G of Stone Section, a consistent pattern in the treatment history emerged. A resident psychiatrist might come to the ward, work intensively with a patient, and finally establish rapport. However, when his training period on Stone Section was completed, the resident then would be transferred to another section, and the patient subsequently usually collapsed into a regressed state. Afterward, another resident or member of the professional staff would again establish rapport and the cycle was repeated. After years of this constant establishing and breaking of emotional ties, patients usually became apathetic and were considered hopeless.

Ten such patients were selected for this project from the forty-five patients on Ward G of Stone Section. With the help of one aide, Mrs. Esther Watts, a "total push" program in which every minute of the day was scheduled for the patients was instituted. Any problems or questions which developed were discussed by the psychologist and Mrs. Watts in a daily meeting.

Initially the psychologist conceived of himself as providing treatment to the patients, with Mrs. Watts assisting him in seeing to it that the patients carried out their activities. Further, her continuous presence provided a figure with which the patients might relate. As the year progressed, however, it became evident that Mrs. Watts' relationship with the patients and her naturally intrusive, spontaneous, and warm style became paramount in patient improvement. Her ability to work with patients, to communicate with them, and to provide for them what they really seemed to need had thoroughly altered the original intent of the pilot study. The psychologist's role had evolved to one of primarily providing support and assistance to Mrs. Watts, rather than directing the patient's treatment.

As the patients improved, other patients on the ward indicated they wanted to be given a similar opportunity. Mrs. Watts commented that though it was hard, her work was very rewarding. Of the fourteen patients treated, six had been discharged and the remaining eight had each made substantial improvement.

It had become apparent that such patients could profit and improve in a situation where a psychiatric aide assumed a central, active treatment role. She was free to relate to patients directively and spontaneously and had the authority commensurate with this type of relationship. It was also evident, however, that she would require a supportive relationship with other members of the staff.

During the course of the pilot study, Dr. Suzanna Reyes, a psychiatrist, was assigned to Stone Section. Since one of her assignments was as ward physician for Ward G, she had abundant opportunity to observe the work of Mrs. Watts. In June 1960 she was assigned as ward physician to Ward H. She was impressed with the similarity of the patient population on H to those of the pilot group. Since Mrs. Watts did so excellently, she wondered if other aides might not be able to conduct similar treatment. The possibility of utilizing a treatment structure similar to the pilot group for Ward H was discussed with the staff on Stone Section. The section staff concurred with the idea and in view of its innovative character it was established as a demonstration project supported by hospital funds. With this then the Ward H project was underway, although with little realization of the eventual scope and implications of the undertaking.

3

Initiating the Project

The setting for the project was Stone Section, which at that time housed seven female wards of approximately thirty-six patients each. One ward on this section, Ward H, had over the years come to be reserved for the most unmanageable, aggressive, and disturbed patients, although the treatment philosophy of the institution no longer segregates patients in this manner. To take care of them, there were four aides on the morning shift, four aides on the afternoon shift, and two aides on the night shift.

The ward had a quality that made it difficult to conceive of positive change taking place. It was not difficult to visualize this ward five years in the future functioning essentially in the same way described here. Some patients would die only to be replaced by similar ones. There might be spontaneous remission in some cases, but this is unlikely with a chronic schizophrenic patient. A few might have been sent off to nursing homes because they no longer required the psychiatric supervision of this kind of ward. But in general there would be little to look forward to.

In many instances these patients of Ward H could be called the therapeutic failures; they had not responded to new treatment procedures and had been separated from the more active treatment wards. On the average they had been in the hospital for ten years or longer. Their care was mainly custodial, partly because professional staffs preferred the challenge of patients with better prognoses, partly because of the great frustration and tolerance necessary to achieve even the most minimal results. Tranquilizers that made other patients more amenable to treatment served only to quiet these patients, sometimes not even that. The problems for the staff on old Ward H were great and the crises frequent, without the commensurate satisfaction that came to other ward staffs.

Physically, the ward was a drab place with scrubbed bare pine flooring, fifteen-foot ceilings, small corridors, and narrow sleeping rooms opening off the 156' × 13' main dayroom. Walls were painted apple green, with similarly colored radiator covers needed to prevent the self-destructive or completely oblivious patient from burning himself on the old-fashioned steam radiators. There was fine wire mesh over the tall narrow windows, plain unindividualized institutional furniture, and an all-pervading aseptic institutional smell.

Because of the high incidence of assaultive behavior, the usual efforts of the staffs on other wards to provide a more homelike atmosphere with such things as curtains, pictures, and tablecloths were not possible on this ward. The personnel on the ward was so involved with emergency and necessary duties that there was neither the time nor the energy left to be concerned with these luxuries.

Based upon their experience in the pilot project, the investigators felt this overall situation could be improved. The changes they were to introduce were eventually to involve drastic alterations of the social and administrative structure of the ward. While many of these were not originally anticipated, they naturally flowed from the basic principles underlying the project.

The first principle developed from the inconsistency evident in the fact that chronic schizophrenics are seen as non-responsible; they are brought to the hospital to become responsible, but there is no one near them behaving in a responsible way whom they can use as a model. The aides, though present, are the end point of a hierarchy, they receive and carry out orders but are not intended to make responsible decisions. The project altered the structure so that the aides might become models for the patients. It was believed that if these patients could be directly cared for by persons who are in the position of formulating policy and making decisions, then the possibility of the patients developing responsibility themselves would be greatly enhanced.

The second principle guiding this project was the overwhelming importance of commitment, devotion, and, above all, spontaneity in the care and treatment of these patients; the nature of their illness made these three qualities absolutely essential. Under the usual system many opportunities for treatment were missed because of the inevitable delay involved in several personnel observing, reporting, and studying a patient's bizarre behavior pattern; when the prescribed response was finally relayed back to the patient the opportune moment for a therapeutic intervention was past. The reaction to these patients must be immediate and spontaneous. But spontaneity and devotion cannot be expected of treatment personnel who in themselves do not feel the responsibility for the treatment of patients nor in any real sense have it. You cannot prescribe devotion and spontaneity, you can only provide the opportunity for its development. In giving the aides the responsibility for treatment, the project permitted them to be spontaneous as well as committed to these patients.

A third guiding principle cannot really be separated from the above but does have other implications. This principle is the belief that one of the greatest resources we have to offer patients is ourselves. There is not sufficient difference between any two people, regardless of the amount of education, the degrees they have, the formal trappings of their status and prestige in society, to differentiate them basically in terms of their capacity to help one another. The inference of this principle is that with a certain amount of guidance and support there is no reason why a psychiatric aide who is on the lowest salary and prestige level of the institution cannot be given the opportunity and does not have the resources to do as much as the person at the other extreme of the status and financial hierarchy of the institution. The potential for development and growth in the aide is as great as that of any other human being and merely requires an optimal structure in order to develop. The project was structured to provide opportunities for development and growth in the psychiatric aide group which would then make new abilities available for the treatment of the patient.

Finally, this effort was set up as a demonstration project with an evolutionary principle: the attempt would be to survey the ongoing interactions, define problems, look at emerging information, measure what was happening, and feed back the results and their conclusions or advice to start a new cycle. It was assumed that making a positive value out of not knowing where you are going creates a climate which involves everyone actively. As an example, rather than giving definite roles to ward staff members, the staff were to evolve their own roles and pragmatically determine who had what responsibility.

IMPLEMENTATION

In July 1960 the Ward H project became a reality. When the work began the directors had first to consider the aides and patients already there. Since all the hospital's aides are carefully screened on the basis of psychological testing, references, and interviews and have all received the training mentioned in Chapter 1, no other selection methods were used to staff the Ward H project. The directors specifically wanted to deal with the aides already on the ward rather than a hand-picked group, so the project results would have more obvious application to the average ward with the average staff.

The aides on the ward at the project's beginning were told of the project's goals and invited to participate. They were told in a general way about intrusive treatment theory. They were told that they would be asked to function in a spontaneous, concrete fashion, and were given some idea of the limits of their new responsibility. With the choice of remaining on the ward for this study, six of the eight assigned to the ward agreed to remain. In addition, Mrs. Watts, who had worked on the pilot project, moved to Ward H.

At the beginning of the project there were transfers among the patient population. While the total ward population of thirty-six patients originally included mostly chronic schizophrenics, there were some patients with organic problems, and some geriatric patients. All the patients who were not diagnosed as chronic schizophrenic were moved to other wards. The eleven vacancies thus created were filled from the population of other wards with patients judged most difficult by other hospital staff.

The first change introduced was to divide the patients

into four groups of nine each. Rather than having the
aides on a shift care for all the patients as a whole, each
aide was to be responsible for one specific group of patients which was to remain hers throughout the course
of the project. Similar arrangements were made on both
the morning and the afternoon shifts. From this point
onward the morning and afternoon aides became partners
in the care of their specific nine patients. The range of
severity of illness found in each group was to reflect the
range present in the total ward population. Within these
limits then the selection of patients for each group, as
well as the selection of partners, was left to the aides. The
next step was to request the superintendent of the institution to delegate the responsibility for the treatment of
these patients directly to the Ward H aides. It became
policy that the aides were to have total treatment responsibility for these patients with no other staff member having contact with them except with the permission of the
responsible aides.

There were two additional reasons for breaking the
group into four parts with an aide for each nine patients.
The directors believed that it would be easier in terms of
time and available psychic energy for the aide to invest
herself in nine patients rather than thirty-six. Also, they
believed it was simpler and more appropriate for this type
of patient to be exposed to only one significant person for
her overall relationship.

Not mentioned in the original formulation of the project, and rarely mentioned thereafter, were the night shift
aides who came on duty at 11:00 P.M. and left at 7:00
A.M. Although they may have influenced the patient's
progress and consequently the results of the project, little
effort was made to incorporate them into the project activities or inculcate them with the project's beliefs.

The ward itself was physically divided into four areas.
Each group was assigned one particular dayhall area. They
would be responsible for its appearance and generally conduct their ward activities there. Since it was assumed by
the project staff that the schizophrenic is prone to rely
on external cues as a guide to behavior, the staff felt it
important that the ward itself be decorated in a way most
conducive to setting up the expectation of healthy behav-

ior in the patients. In accordance with this idea they planned to make cooking facilities available on the ward, as well as radios, full-length mirrors, chiming clocks, bulletin boards, blackboards, and anything else that might be used to increase the patients' sensory awareness of the environment.

Formal training sessions were conducted daily by Dr. Reyes and the project directors. These sessions were recorded for later study and discussion with the aides. Techniques of treatment consistent with the theory were demonstrated.

The ideas and goals of this project were explained to groups of the other staff members at Topeka State Hospital. The staff presentations were held to explain what was planned on the project and what might be anticipated in the future. The initial reaction of these groups to the project was quite favorable and enthusiastic. As will be seen later, this positive reaction was not maintained and within a year the project became alienated and isolated from the total organization.

The innovations in the treatment structure on Ward H necessitated changes and suspension of a number of hospital policies and procedures as they might apply to the ward. It was evident that the partner aides would need to work closely together. To facilitate their working relationship, a request was made of Nursing Service that the shift hours of the Ward H nurse be changed from 8:00 to 5:00 so that she might overlap shifts with both the morning and afternoon aides. This would allow her to have contact with both shifts and would provide for the possibility of consistent supervision of the two aide partners.

At the project's beginning Dr. Reyes and the project directors each spent about four hours a day on the ward, two hours in meetings, and two hours just moving around the ward getting to know people. Also they were always on call. Efforts were made to contact others in the hospital who were involved in making decisions about patients and to inform them about the project. The exploratory nature of the project required the ward staff and others outside the ward to refrain from unilateral decision making. Rule-making propensities had to be curbed, since once rules are made there is no need to exercise judgment. A valued norm on Ward H became the promotion of growth and participation, discussion and exploration, rather than the use of rules and precedent.

There were many other ways in which hospital structure was changed to accommodate the project. When discussions and the experience of the pilot project indicated that some hospital rules and regulations seemed antithetical to the project's philosophy, the superintendent in a memo gave this ward permission to deviate from established policies. The exceptions agreed upon were:

(1) Aides could come back to the ward after working hours whenever they wanted to visit patients;
(2) Aides could take patients for rides in their cars;
(3) Aides could invite patients to their homes;
(4) Aides could permit patients to use the keys to the ward;
(5) Aides could initiate money-making projects with patients;
(6) Patients could answer the ward phone;
(7) Aides would be permitted to eat on the ward with the patients if such contact was therapeutically desirable.

Hospital policy did not provide for leaves of absence for aides in case of pregnancy. Ward H aides were allowed to return and work part time if they wished to do so.

In matters of policy, discussion and negotiation was the goal, rather than unilateral decision and directive.

ROLES

Again the evolutionary nature of this project must be stressed. The directors began with few ideas other than these: there were specific kinds of patients to be treated, a treatment theory that seemed appropriate, and a belief that aides could carry out the responsibility for this treatment. Beyond that, everything was tentative. Procedures that were finally used were the result of two or three that failed. Minor innovations could become giant steps; major ones dismal failures.

Perhaps nowhere was this philosophy more evident

than in the redefinition and redelineation of roles. The original ideas of the directors concerned two broad categories, the role of the aide and that of the other professional staff on the ward. This latter group included the physician, nurse, social workers, adjunctive therapists, and volunteers. During the first year the role of the aide received the greatest attention because the guiding principles of the project made this role crucial, and it became evident that the roles of others would be determined by what was evolved here.

The directors attempted to develop an administrative structure that would facilitate the task of role development through various meetings, workshops, and consultations, with the hope that within this framework evolution and progressive discovery of limits would give the role the substance and structure needed. This development had the consistent aim of defining the roles in terms of responsibility and accountability, not specific functions.

The initial tentative expectations for the role of the aide were:

(a) To accept responsibility for the treatment of the patient, since in this project treatment is seen as occurring primarily in the aide-patient relationship. It is hoped that the aide can develop responsibility for making observations of the patient, formulating these observations into problems, and seeking solution for these problems which she can then apply to the treatment of the patient. In the seeking for solutions she will be encouraged to use her own initiative, and to utilize the daily training sessions with the other aides, the project directors, and the ward nurse. The emphasis upon formulating problems and applying solutions to patient treatment by individual initiative differentiates the aide's role in this project from her ordinary one in this hospital. During the early phases of the project the emphasis will be primarily upon the aide's reviewing her observations and treatment plans in the daily training sessions. As she gains more competence with the therapeutic approach and a more complete knowledge of her patients, she will be more strongly encouraged to use her own initiative. In short, the goal of the project is helping the aide gradually to assume full responsibility for the treatment of the patient.

(b) To provide a reality figure with whom the patient may identify.

(c) To intrude into the consciousness of the patient and make her presence felt, thereby strengthening the patient's contact with reality.

(d) By the use of intrusion therapy to aid the patient in establishing the limits and boundaries of her own body.

(e) To encourage and assist the patient to accept as much responsibility for herself as possible.

(f) To keep the necessary records on all patients in the aide's particular group.

(g) To structure and schedule the patient's activities in keeping with the treatment aims of the project.

(h) When possible to establish relationships with the patient's family and/or community.

Independence and development were to be fostered. The only two reasons projected as sufficient for dismissal were uncooperativeness with the other aides or gross irresponsibility. In all other instances of difficulties the entire project staff devoted themselves to encouraging the aide's capacities for assuming responsibility.

Instead of being an end-point in a series of orders and prescriptions, the aide was to be permitted to act in the hospital as the same responsible, capable force she was in her family and her community. She was encouraged to demonstrate interest and was instructed in a treatment theory as a frame of reference, while offered continuing support and advice from the other members of the project. Given these opportunities, the hope was to discover the limits of this approach in evoking the patient's capacity to assume responsibility again, and at the same time to see what kind of limits there were to the aide's capacity to take this kind of responsibility.

For this project, the task was to guide the patient's capacity for growth to the point where he could assume the social responsibilities he had abandoned or never developed. The aide was the instrument of this rehabilitation since by her reactions and attitudes toward the patient she was to offer the patient a personality to be emulated. The factors used in determining who may be therapeutic to a a patient are availability, natural ability, knowledge of a science, and experience or knowledge of life. In the usual selection process, knowledge of a science has been considered the preeminent criterion. Availability, experience of life, and natural ability, usually considered of lesser importance, became all-important for this project. Rather than emphasizing that the secret of success in treatment is knowing the cause of mental illness, i.e., knowledge is power, the assumption here was that success derives from the quality of the relationship between people, or engagement is power. Fostering this engagement on the part of the aide, then, was the task of the project.

With these steps the project was initiated. In postulating the task of the project to promote the growth and development of the patients, the directors felt that a similar positive change must be encouraged in everyone in the project since all of them were to serve in one way or another as models for those around them. All were to be given opportunities for experimenting with their abilities and their roles, permitted flexibility and offered guidance, so that those who were dedicated to growth might also grow themselves.

This then was the embryo which was to develop over the next four years.

4

The First Year—The Aide

The project can be viewed as an historical process developing in phases. Each phase was characterized by the salience of certain issues which demanded understanding, problem definition, and problem solution. Viewed from another perspective perhaps one might say that the project went through a growth process. The various phases represented a maturation in the thinking, sophistication, and competence of the project group. In retrospect, it becomes apparent that all of the problems were present at any one time and that perhaps the determining factor in the choice of which problem was to be actively worked upon was that of saliency or relevancy to the project's viability and growth.

Consequently, the major issue during the first year was the performance and the motivation of the aides. They had been asked to participate in an endeavor which was radically to alter their roles. There were many questions about their capability to handle the task that had been asked of them. Perhaps an even more important question than their competence for the task was their motivation —were they willing to commit themselves to these extraordinarily exacting patients; were they willing to commit themselves to the amount of time, energy, work, and learning that would be necessary for them in their new role. If they were not, there could be no project. It was this question that became the focus of the first year of the project. While other questions and problems were held in abeyance the project staff concerned itself with the exploration, understanding, and description of the aides' experience of their new role.

In retrospect it has become obvious that a great deal of growth took place in the aides during this first year and that the growth proceeded in an orderly manner through three distinct phases. At each stage, new and significant behaviors became evident. This is not to indicate that the behaviors from the previous phases had completely dropped away; quite the contrary, many of them still remained and on superficial observation one would be hard put to say that any changes had occurred at all. However, upon closer scrutiny, it becomes apparent that extremely significant changes in the aides' personal experience of themselves were occurring. While this new self-concept was frequently fragile and tentative, it had occurred within the context of the project and it provided for the entire project staff a reinforcement of their own investment in the potentials of the aides. For the aides themselves it provided new standards of behavior and self-experience which they vigorously worked to maintain.

PHASE ONE—THE FIRST THREE MONTHS

The Aides' Initial Experience of Their New Role

The aides began their new tasks with considerable enthusiasm. Although they felt uncertain and insecure about the exact details of the future, professionals now were showing an interest in them and letting them show what they could do. There was an emphasis on their patients' improvement, but there was an equal emphasis on their own importance. To be given authority was a unique experience. Realization of the consequent responsibility naturally took longer to grow, and as it did it tended to provoke marked anxiety.

During the first period of the project's life, the theme might have been "crisis." According to one of the project directors, "Dr. Reyes and I were always on call. For the first year I don't think there was a day that I didn't get some kind of call at home." Crises occurred daily. Almost any event, no matter how small, no matter how realistically insignificant it was to the project, seemed to loom as a crisis. A negative reaction on the part of a nonproject staff member, a delay on the part of a department head in dealing with a Ward H request, even restrained, sober criticism was immensely threatening during this initial period; such reactions were experienced as an obstacle to the project's progress. There were few of these events that were in reality crises in the life of the project, but it became apparent that they were experienced as crises by the aides. In each of these the expectation on their part was that the project directors needed "to do something about" the crises. If the directors were unable to intervene actively, the aides experienced a sense of helplessness and a feeling of lack of support from the hospital for their new role. To quote from a progress report compiled early in the project:

There were many of the personnel throughout the hospital who did have occasional contact with Ward H but who were unfamiliar with the new structure. These people included such individuals as the OD, the evening shift chief nurse, and various consultants. When these individuals did have contact with Ward H and responded to it in much the same manner as they would to other wards in the hospital, the aides would not make an effort to explain that they were working under a different system or to orient the newcomer to Ward H procedures. Rather, they would respond to this as another indication of lack of support on the part of the hospital and would then make an "emergency" phone call to one of the project directors.

One evening one of the project directors received a phone call at home from one of the aides. The aide complained that the OD had visited the ward, had seen that one of the patients was disturbed and had ordered the patient placed in seclusion. She then went on to indicate that she did not feel that her patient needed to be in seclusion. When asked whether she explained this to the ward physician she indicated that she had not; he had "ordered" her to. Again when asked if she had explained the arrangement and different structure on Ward H, she indicated that she had not. The project director then indicated that she should do so, but that he would call the OD and inform him.

The crisis is one method of making a bridge between individuals when no satisfactory personal relationship exists. Among normal individuals who are exhibiting a fair amount of awareness, a satisfactory relationship implies sensitivity to one another's needs and therefore the crisis-producing cry for help is frequently an effort to test the mutuality of sensitivity.

Crisis communication proved to have its adaptive use; it provided an action-oriented means whereby the aides could test their relationship to the staff and to the patients. They were very much concerned with their actual and real authority over the patients. On the one hand they communicated the feeling that they "didn't know what to do." They were somewhat reluctant to "stick their necks out." They were very uncertain whether they had really been given the authority; and, if they had, they were as yet unsure how well they could use it or would be supported in its use. As a consequence they required a great deal of encouragement to initiate activity with the patient or to begin to have a meaningful influence on her.

At other times the aides would overreact to their authority. They would become extremely possessive of their patients and regard any efforts on the part of the staff to review with them their relationship with their patients, or their patients' activities, as a diminution of their authority. As further tests of this authority, some intensely dramatic interchanges would occur between them and their patients that had a certain amount of shock value for the hospital and again had the potential for producing crises.

Hilda was a young, heavy-set woman in her late twenties who had been hospitalized at Topeka State for approximately eight years. During those years her behavior was characterized by near-mutism, extreme negativism and combative episodes that were almost daily in frequency. She had rapidly attained and consistently maintained a "reputation" throughout the hospital as a "tough battler." Frequently it would be necessary to call male aides from other wards to help in quieting Hilda or to place her in seclusion. On a day a few months after the project's inception Hilda approached her afternoon aide, Mrs. M., and asked that she be permitted to go to her bedroom and sleep. Mrs. M. indicated that Hilda had some ward assignments to do and should do these first. With this Hilda became very angry, picked up a large chair and threw it across the room, and then began to wrestle with Mrs. M. As they fell to the floor wrestling, the other aides on the ward began to come to Mrs. M.'s aid. Mrs. M. indicated that they were not to help her; she felt it was important for her to handle Hilda herself. She stated that if Hilda could not come to realize that Mrs. M. was able to handle her that she, Mrs. M., would not be of any help to her. They wrestled about for approximately an hour and a half and finally ended up with Mrs. M. sitting astraddle Hilda. Within a few days the event had become known

throughout much of the hospital and there was much negative comment about Mrs. M. wrestling with Hilda for this
period of time and about the chances that she had taken in
doing so.

During this period efforts at adapting to their new relationship with the ward staff took on a similar form of
testing. At best, this relationship could be defined as
"touchy." The aides were sensitive to anything which
could be construed as criticism or as a return on the part
of the ward staff to the old aide-staff relationships. To
suggest an alternate way of relating to a patient or an
alternate activity was to imply that the aide was "wrong"
in the way that she was currently dealing with the patient. After each of these events a period of "hurt feelings" would ensue.

Another type of behavior that was evident in the aide's
relationship to the staff was what the staff came to call
"trapping." Generally this involved the aide's nonsupport
of a staff member, usually in an effort to test that staff
member's commitment to the project goals and to the
aide's new role. Frequently when some decision would be
called for, the aides would usually refuse to participate in
making the decision and would thereby create a vacuum
in an effort to see whether or not the staff would step
into the vacuum and make a decision without their participation. For example,

early in the project it had become obvious that there was
a need for daily meetings between the aides and the project
staff to orient ourselves to the goals of the project, its approaches and techniques. The aides agreed that such a meeting was necessary and were asked to come to some decision
as a group as to the frequency, duration and structure of the
meetings. The staff waited approximately two weeks for
them to decide but no decision was forthcoming. When
pressed about it, they offered little. Finally the project staff
set up an hourly meeting from 10:00 to 11:00 in the morning and met with the aides each weekday morning. A short
time later the staff began to hear many complaints about
this meeting—it was too time consuming, it did not really
meet their needs, they were not really interested in hearing
about other people's patients, the content was not of any
use to them. When asked again if they wished to restructure
it, there were very few constructive suggestions. This, despite

the fact that they all appeared to look forward to the daily meeting and participated in it quite well.

Another area of "touchiness" was evident whenever members of the staff attempted to give advice to the aides. While the advice was offered to the aide with the provision that the aide was free to accept or reject it, the aides initially responded to these efforts as though they were orders given by the staff. Frequently in discussing a patient with an aide the staff might offer something like "Well, one thing you might try would be to . . ." only later on to have the aide come back to the staff member indicating that she had done what the staff person had advised but didn't really think it was a good idea. When asked then why she had done it, the response was usually "Well, you told me to."

This behavior was manifest also in the aides' relationships to their consultants. When during one of his visits Dr. DesLauriers expressed an interest in a certain kind of data on the aide-patient relationship, the aides made a list of things to include in their report and ended up spending two hours a day in such work. The size of this task soon overwhelmed the aides, and they complained bitterly about having to do what had been asked of them. It was pointed out that it had not really been asked of them, that they had acted on their own to provide the data the consultant had been interested in. Despite this, however, it took concerted effort on the part of all to get the aides to give up this task.

Such occurrences were frequent especially when the consultant involved was in somewhat of a supervisory position and might be called on to evaluate an aide's worth and work. At a conference with the doctor a pair of the aides presented one of their patients. They had decided that the patient was going home for a visit on the weekend. The doctor commented that he thought this was not a good idea and that it would be better if the patient stayed in the hospital. When one of the aides came back to the ward she grumbled because she had decided that the patient was going to go home. "And now," she complained, "the doctor says I can't send the patient home." It was pointed out by the nurse that she did not have to do what the doctor said. Whether she sent the patient home was something she had to decide for herself because she knew the patient better than anyone else. It was her responsibility, however, to consider what the consultant had advised and use this new information, but the final decision was hers. As time went on, more frequent use of the consultant staff made the aides aware that even authorities could disagree. This was an idea that they found upsetting at first and then amusing. For several months any minor difference of opinion was magnified and conflicts were frequent.

Another area frequently tested during this initial phase in terms of the aides' relationship to the staff was that of mutual goal setting and planning. Frequently the aides complained that they were not involved in ward and project planning. They would often indicate that they were not aware of decisions recently made or would question who had made a decision. This despite the fact that much effort was made to involve them in planning. Frequently it appeared that, even though they had been originally involved in the planning, they would be unable to recall this later on. Quite the contrary, they would complain that they had not been involved or that they thought the decision arrived at was a different one.

The aides were also very eager to experiment regarding their care of the patients and the ward. Initially this interest was demonstrated in some physical changes on the ward. The aides felt that the architecture of the ward in itself had a depressing effect upon both themselves and the patients; they complained of the color of the walls, the lack of furniture, and the inconvenience of the physical arrangements. Together the aides and the ward staff began a series of discussions about how the ward might be arranged more adequately. From these talks came initially a series of requests that were realistically impossible for the institution to fulfill because of limited resources for maintenance and capital improvement. Over a period of time, however, the aides were able to accept these limitations and work within them, and very slowly physical changes consistent with the treatment needs of the patients began to occur on the ward.

In addition to attempting changes on the ward, they began to experiment with some of the new alternative activities for their patients. They began to take patients for rides in their cars. They began to see some of the patients' relatives and talk with them. They began sending patients off the ward and away from the hospital on passes at their own initiative. When they had patients off the ward or off the hospital campus and patients became upset, the aides would try to handle the disturbance on the spot rather than immediately bringing the patient back to the ward. It was the general impression of the staff that these attempts at new activities were not initiated so much in terms of the aides' relationship to the patient but rather to experiment with them and test out staff and hospital reaction to their engaging in these activities. Only when they had assured themselves of staff approval did they feel secure in using these techniques as a treatment modality.

Despite all these positive aspects, however, the underlying tone of the aides' reaction was one of pessimism, pessimism about the hospital's commitment to their new role, pessimism about the capacity of the project staff to support them sufficiently and to work out the difficulties caused by their new role in the hospital. Above all, there was pessimism about the capacity of the patients to improve. Whenever their patients were discussed in meetings with the ward staff, the aides would convey a sense of futility about working with them. Frequently the comment was made, "These patients are hopeless"; or "That patient will never get well." The aides frequently voiced the feeling that they were being asked to invest a great deal in patients for whom the likelihood of improvement was minimal; it would be better to use their time and investment on patients who might get well more rapidly and for whom the probabilities of improvement were higher. On the other hand, whenever the aides were offered opportunities to work with such a hopeful patient, they generally offered the opposite point of view. Instead, they would point out that for those patients for whom there was a good probability of improvement, the usual ward routine seemed to work well; it was the chronic patient, the regressed patient, who really needed human contact, above all, that offered by their aides.

By virtue of their behavior, then, the aides appeared to

be extremely sensitive to the demands of their new role. Their behavior usually communicated, on the one hand, their own anxieties about their adequacy, and, on the other hand, a plea for help and support so that they would do well.

The change in roles aroused a great deal of anxiety. The aides seemed to feel trapped; they felt that their added responsibilities placed them in a position where they were extremely dependent on the professional staff. At the same time, they were not always sure of the extent to which the professional staff understood their needs or the extent to which they themselves could trust them. They perceived themselves as extremely exposed and vulnerable. If they were really to accept their new role, their errors in judgment, personality defects, and frustrations would become evident in their treatment of the patients. They would be open to criticism, rebuff, and rejection. While they were challenged by the new role and their earnest desire was to accept it and to do well, nevertheless they felt highly threatened and in jeopardy. During the early months of the project the aides exhibited a constant free-floating anxiety which was adaptively drained off through action and through testing out their relationships to the patients, the ward staff, and the hospital as a whole.

Sources of Aides' Anxiety

Given the presence of intense anxiety on the part of the aides, what were the sources of this reaction to their new role? Certainly one source was found in the departure from the traditional role of the aide at the hospital. Seldom before had aides been given this kind of direct treatment authority and responsibility because the aide was supposed to lack the training to deal with the patient's problems. Her capacity to be of help to patients was seen as extremely limited in any therapeutic sense. Her former role was primarily that of a custodial person; her responsibilities were not previously defined in terms of persons or patients, but rather in terms of function, that is, the protection of the patient from himself and provision for his physical care. Under these circumstances there were several factors that precluded the aides becoming emotionally involved with the patient or the patient's problems. First of all, they tended to operate under what was largely a negative reward system. In the event of an elopement, the aide usually perceived herself as responsible for the breach of security. Incidents of physical violence or destruction of property were considered situations for which the aide might be personally liable and administratively accountable. The aide was distracted from personal attachment because of the time required in maintaining custodial functions. To some extent the ideal accomplishment was simply to get through another day without an incident or crisis.

Even if these factors had not prevailed, there were few positive rewards for the aide's extra investment of time and energy in her patients. The aide tended to receive little credit for efforts toward the patient's improvement; and to some extent involvement with the patient was taboo. First, active participation by the aide was seen as interfering with the patient's relationship with the physician; and, second, such an involvement might permit a return to the old state hospital situation of exploitation of patients by aides. This attitude of the hospital about the aide-patient interaction stemmed from a well-intentioned effort to protect both the aide and the patient. As a consequence, any personal interest that an aide demonstrated in a patient was to some extent illicit. The support necessary to sustain prolonged concern and involvement with the patient was usually not offered. Consequently, these traditions of the aide group at the hospital mitigated against close involvement with the patient or the professional staff, the assumption of authority and accountability, and the acceptance of responsibility for the patient as a person. To some extent professional staff and aides had traditionally been seen as two different kinds of persons, each with their own value system and their own particular approach to life: the approach of one made them valuable as custodial personnel, the approach of the other as therapeutic personnel. The capacity of the aide to be consistently and responsibly therapeutic had long been untested because it was assumed that they couldn't be.

All of the aides involved in the project at its inception,

of course, had worked at the hospital under the old system and under the old traditions. Some had been there as long as fourteen years; others only two, but in the process all had become indoctrinated in these traditions.

The discrepancy between old habits and new expectations was not the only source of anxiety for the aides. There was much in the new situation itself that tended to engender and sustain anxiety. First of all, it must be remembered that one of the goals was to permit the project to structure itself around the role of the aides as the primary treatment agents of the patients. To a large extent what their needs might be was quite unknown, and consequently, the project made a positive value of not knowing. The old traditions, roles, ways of operating, problem solving, and ward management had been discarded and nothing except a deliberate chaos was left in their place. It was only as the aides were able in either words or action to articulate their needs, the kinds of support necessary and the problems they encountered, that a new structure would be evolved, based upon their special needs and concerns.

Consequently, during the early months of the project a structural vacuum had been created on the ward, a vacuum that could not be filled immediately because it was only with the passage of time that structural needs would become obvious. Even though the aides were very much action-oriented, there were no directives for action. Their roles had previously been defined in terms of functions or actions and yet in this situation the only prescription for action was extremely vague and generalized, that is, "treat the patient."

The previous treatment programs for the patients had been disrupted. They, too, were in a state of chaos or confusion. Because previous industrial assignments, adjunctive therapy activities, passes, and drug regimes had all been disrupted, the patients tended to react strongly. During this period the patients attempted to test in various ways just what the structure was; thus, while the ward staff had to tolerate the testing on the part of the aides, the aides had to tolerate testing on the part of the patients. The patients initially seemed quite concerned about the aides having authority over them. They too were used to the notion that only the doctors had authority. They would corner visitors to the ward and complain to them about not having the doctor to talk to, about the aides being "over them," about being treated by Negroes, about the lack of activity, "about the terrible things aides had done to them."

There was little in this situation that provided any degree of comfort for the aides. The aides' lack of confidence in their own abilities was only heightened by the patients' lack of confidence in them, and it soon became apparent to them that the patients' respect and regard would be earned slowly.

There was further lack of structure in terms of a means for problem solving. Previously there had been formal and informal channels of communication for problems, and meetings were oriented toward handling these problems. These were channels that all knew about; because such means for approaching and resolving problems did exist, all felt a certain degree of security. Again, these channels, too, had been disrupted; in the early months there was no evidence to indicate what were the best means of communication, what needed to be communicated to whom, or what types of meetings should be held.

A further area of vagueness was, of course, the delineation of authority and responsibility. Again, in the old structure this was clear-cut; there was a policies and procedures manual that usually let most people know what their responsibilities were and what their authority was. Again on the project this was unclear. There were only vague statements about who was responsible for what kinds of problems. The statement had been made that the aides were responsible for patients, and yet just what did this responsibility entail, what were its limits? Were they responsible when they felt they couldn't handle a situation? Were they responsible when problems involved the community? Were they responsible when their work involved families? In the past at this point these decisions usually were the responsibility of the professional staff. How would the professional staff react now? All of these questions lacked definitions and answers. If the aides were responsible for patients, who was responsible for the ward? Who was responsible for deciding what the aides needed? What kind of planning should go on and who should do it? There were no answers, and perhaps, what was even more anxiety provoking, was that initially there weren't even these questions. Only with the passage of time would these issues and questions become obvious and then solutions could be attempted.

In their efforts to free themselves from the traditions of their old roles and to try to understand and elaborate their new roles, the aides were not always fully abetted by the project or the hospital staff. For these people, too, new roles were necessary and old habits were strong. Under the pressure of stress and time old habits frequently returned and the ward staff found itself functioning in a way which was discrepant with the stated aims of the project.

Ann was an extremely paranoid patient who was overtly hallucinatory and delusional. Despite this, however, to the casual observer she could present a "good front." Her parents had long been separated and each of them seemed to be involved in a battle with the hospital to get Ann released from the hospital. Ann was on voluntary status and the aides felt that the structure was indeed a difficult one in which to attempt treatment. Shortly after the beginning of the project Ann eloped from the hospital and went to her father's home. This was discussed on the ward and there was a general consensus with the aides feeling that she should not be permitted to return unless she was returned on a committed status. Mrs. Jones, her morning aide, was to get in contact with the father and convey this information to him. Shortly after Mrs. Jones' phone call the father called Dr. Reyes, the ward doctor, and indicated that he was unwilling to bring Ann back on a committed status, but that, however, if she could remain on voluntary, he would willingly bring her back in two days. Dr. Reyes agreed to this. When she communicated this to Mrs. Jones and Mrs. Nelson, the afternoon aide, they both became extremely angry with Dr. Reyes and pointed out that she had made a decision that was supposed to be theirs and that was, in fact, contradictory to theirs. They indicated that they felt that she was not supporting them in terms of the project goals and the role that had been set up for them. Dr. Reyes was somewhat taken aback by their initial reaction and indicated that it was a situation in which some compromise was necessary. The aides felt that any compromise would make the treatment situation untenable for them. After some discussion, Dr. Reyes was able to agree that she had indeed taken the responsibility for the decision out of their hands and had placed the aides in a difficult situation. In her further contacts with the family she supported the aides' position and when Ann did return to the hospital she was returned on a committed status.

There was no doubt that the project staff intended to encourage decision making and independence by the aides. It was only that habit was so strong; the staff was used to making decisions for the aides and the aides were accustomed to accepting such decisions. Overcoming this pattern was an uphill fight. The greatest source of help in dealing with this problem was the fact that the nurse and the physician on the ward did not know the patients well and the aides were forced to act at least as mediums of communication. Despite this, however, there were occasions when the role expectations of the aides communicated verbally by the staff were quite inconsistent with that demonstrated by their behavior.

This problem was evident not only in terms of the relationship of the aides to the project staff but equally so in terms of their relationship to the remainder of the hospital. Certainly there had been a consensus within the hospital of the worth of the project and the merit of an exploration of the limits of the aides' new role. However, when situations on H were responded to by hospital staff in a manner consistent with the old role of the aides, but certainly inconsistent with the aides' new role, the aides again experienced this as a lack of support. In most instances this occurred again because of force of habit or lack of communication with nonproject hospital staff, but for the aides in the midst of their struggle, this indeed had a great deal of personal meaning. It meant that others were not fully supportive of their efforts or that others did not have confidence in their capabilities.

Alice, a middle-aged patient who had been at the hospital a number of years, was given to frequent bouts of ranting and raving around the ward. She seemed to know well what she was doing. Usually these bouts followed the denial of some privilege at which point it appeared that she would "throw a tantrum." The effect of her behavior, however, was usually to greatly disturb the ward. The afternoon aides were particularly concerned about her effect on the ward and after some discussion arrived at the decision that the next time she was to do this that she would be told that the ward was her home as well as the home of others, and that at home people simply did not upset the situation as she was doing. Consequently, if she wanted to do this she was to be asked to leave the ward and she would be free to rant and rave on the grounds where she would disturb no one. This occurred one afternoon at approximately 5:00. Alice was indeed surprised when the aides' thinking was communicated to her and when she was asked to leave the ward, but she left quite docilely. In a few minutes, however, a phone call was received from the hospital's canteen. It seemed that Alice had entered the canteen while many of the evening shift employees were eating their supper and was "throwing her tantrum" there. After this event the project director was approached by the section nurse who felt that it would be necessary to impose some rules about the situations under which patients could be asked to leave the ward. Most especially she was concerned about the time of day. It was her feeling that it was not safe to permit such a patient to roam about the hospital grounds this late in the afternoon when there were very few patients and personnel about. It was pointed out to the nurse that it would not be useful to set rules. If we did, the patients would simply wait until that particular time of the day before they would "act up." She was then asked if she felt that this type of handling of the patient was responsible or not. She indicated that she did not feel it was responsible. It was then pointed out to her that she was free to go to the ward and communicate her feelings to the aides and discuss the situation with them in the hope that either they could help her clarify her thinking or that she could help clarify theirs. But it was indicated that to set a rule would only deprive the aides of an opportunity to learn more responsible forms of treatment behavior from her and others.

In dealing with the aides the use of negotiation and accountability rather than rule-setting presented difficulties for both the hospital and project staff.

Other factors present in the situation were racial, educational, and socioeconomic class differences. Most of the aides were Negroes, high school graduates, and members of a lower socioeconomic class strata. Traditionally, however, patients, relatives, the community at large, and the hospital staff were used to highly educated, middle-class professionals being "in charge of" patients. Consequently, this issue of class and educational, as well as racial, differences, was raised repeatedly. The aides were seen as representing lower-class values which influenced the directions they gave and the things they said to patients. The hospital staff was generally aware that certain social-psychological studies had indicated that staff from the lower socioeconomic classes could most effectively understand or help lower socioeconomic class patients as most of the Ward H patients were. This awareness was not true, however, of the patients, their relatives or the community at large. Consequently, at the project's beginning there were frequent complaints about treatment being conducted by relatively uneducated Negro non-professionals. These complaints at a time of mounting racial tensions over bombings in Alabama and frequent civil rights strife could only increase the uncomfortable aspects of the Ward H arrangement.

Martha was a whiny, cynical patient. She had a way of screwing up her face to let you know the world was a great big lemon and anytime any part of it got inside her it was sour. She herself seemed to be all puckered up and dry. Mrs. Jones, her aide, had difficulty in getting through this cynicism. Martha held Mrs. Jones off, letting her know that whatever she did was not going to be good enough.

A few months after the project began, Martha's mother decided to visit the ward. She wanted to find out what the whole project was about; obviously she was coming for an inspection. She did not approve of aides caring for the patients and she wanted to establish with dispatch who was boss. This maneuver was typical of her relationship with Martha. So Mrs. Jones, Martha, her mother, and the ward nurse met together in the visiting room on the ward. Martha's mother soon lit into Mrs. Jones with a vengeance. She intimated in many different ways that Mrs. Jones could not possibly treat Martha; after all, she was only an aide, she had no formal training; she did not even belong to their class of people. There were many reflections upon the fact that Mrs. Jones was Negro.

Much of this negative criticism reached Mrs. Jones. She absorbed the beating she was taking, and she probably was hit in every vulnerable spot. But most impressive was the way she was able to stand her ground in spite of this battering. Very quietly but also very firmly she informed the mother that whether she liked it or not, or whether she really felt Mrs. Jones was capable or not, she was treating Martha. The doctors felt that Mrs. Jones was capable, she had been given this responsibility, and she was going to handle it.

The first issue over which they disagreed was whether or not Martha would go home for a weekend pass. Mrs. Jones did not feel it was warranted in terms of the mother's attitude and her own lack at this time of a helpful relationship with Martha. Mrs. Jones firmly told the mother that she wouldn't let Martha go home now, but that at some time in the future, once they were getting along better, she would give her a pass; for the moment the answer was no. At that point the mother became even more derogatory and abusive toward Mrs. Jones. But Mrs. Jones did not give in.

After it was all over and the mother had left, Martha told Mrs. Jones that she obviously must care about her if she was able to take all of that abuse from her mother rather than submitting. After this crisis we began to see changes in Martha. She was closer to Mrs. Jones and seemed to have a more trusting attitude.

Finally, of course, the aides brought to the project their own personal fears and anxieties. Frequently these fears, together with the anxiety generated by tradition and the realistic aspects of the situation in and of itself, were played out upon the stage of the Ward H project. The aides, too, certainly had questions about authority and their own adequacy. As most people when first placed in the position of considerable authority and responsibility, they were faced with numerous self-doubts and questioned whether they wished to place themselves in such a vulnerable position. Perhaps most of all they were concerned with placing themselves in a position where any personal weaknesses and inadequacies might be exposed.

Reaction of the Project Staff to Aides' Anxiety

This was the situation which was presented to the project directors and the ward staff. The question became one of how to deal with this situation. It might be stated initially that to a great extent they were largely unaware of the meaning of the aides' anxiety; there were only glimmers of awareness of the extent to which the situation and the alteration of hospital traditions were generating anxiety. As clinicians, they were somewhat more aware of the anxiety generated by the personal meaning of the project to each of the aides rather than the sociological aspects of the situation. In general, however, the staff did not respond to each of these incidents or crises during these first few months as symptoms of an underlying anxiety; rather, they were responded to at face value, that is, as real problems to be dealt with.

It was only in retrospect that it became apparent that this was the best means of response, one acceptable to the aides and seen by them as supportive. It soon became evident that the traditional verbal means of support, that is, the recognition of underlying feelings, simply did not work. The underlying anxiety was much too raw, too strong, too threatening to be openly acknowledged by a group of individuals who had habitually dealt with it in action-oriented terms. Those instances where verbal support was attempted precipitated either anger or an overwhelming sense of helplessness in the aides.

Dr. B, an assistant section chief on Stone Section, had agreed to fill in on the consulting staff while the doctor on the project was on vacation. Dr. B was an extremely sensitive, empathetic individual who was particularly gifted at picking up others' feelings and providing them with feedback on these underlying feelings. He met one day with Mrs. Ross and Mrs. Lewis and they began to discuss one of their more difficult patients. This was a patient who had held them at arms length for quite some time. In their discussion they conveyed their own sense of frustration in dealing with the patient, but even more they conveyed their deep awareness of the patient's sense of loneliness, hopelessness and alienation. Dr. B began to pick up on this and indicated that he heard the aides saying that this was an extremely lonely patient who thought of herself as hopeless and who really didn't feel that she was worth being helped. He continued in this manner to verbalize the feelings of both the aides and the patient. At this point both aides burst out crying and indicated that that was precisely how they felt about the patient; that she was indeed pathetic and what made it so bad was that they could not reach her. Dr. B's initial reaction was one of shock and yet he continued to try to work with these feelings. Talking about it seemed only to intensify them and he seemed quite unable to help the aides get more distance from it. The conference broke up early. Dr. B later on communicated his surprise and his sense of helplessness in dealing with these overwhelming feelings on the part of the aides and indicated he had expected that helping the aides to ventilate their feelings would clear things up; quite the contrary, it had only intensified it.

Except in specific instances the nonutility of traditional verbal support was true throughout the life of the project. Support for the aides was generally obtained through non-verbal, action-oriented means; through an open, spontaneous relationship, the staff expressed its trust in the aide's potential and competence and a respect for his person.

Thus, the project staff soon began to develop a pattern of supporting the aides by concrete demonstrations of regard and help. More specifically, this support was first and foremost constantly available. The project directors were on call, their home phone numbers were available, and whenever needed by the aides they demonstrated their willingness to return to the hospital and talk with them. Consequently, the norm soon developed that the aides were to be provided with informal, individual consultation at any time on request, and this was usually supplemented later on by group discussions with the aides.

Another form of support was the acceptance of the aides' definition of problems. Rather than focusing upon their own personal experiences of these problems, the effort was made to resolve them in an action-oriented manner. When conflicts arose between the aides and the maintenance crew, the nursing service, or the state fire marshal, for example, the aides had the backing of the project staff. Moreover, there were efforts to resolve these problems in a manner that was consistent with the needs of the aides in terms of their new role. In each instance where there was an alteration of previous policies or procedures, the aides accepted the change as an indication of the hospital's support and the capacity of the project staff to both get this support for them and protect them from thoughtless or habitual disruptive incursions into their new role.

When it became evident that some of the hospital policies and procedures were not consistent with the aides' role as defined in this project, the directors talked with the hospital superintendent indicating which of these procedures were inconsistent and requested that they be abrogated for the project. Shortly thereafter a memo was received on the ward from the superintendent listing the policies under discussion and suspending them for the aides on Ward H. The aides reacted to this jubilantly; however, they saw this not only as a manifestation of support on the part of the hospital, but also as an indication of the "cleverness" of the directors in "talking people into things."

Certainly the offering of in-service training to the aides demonstrated profound support; most obviously, such assistance provided the aides with some alternatives to action in dealing with their patients and with a certain amount of theoretical background to help them understand the patients' ordeal, and to justify their own activities with patients. The aspect of training that was most supportive in the long run, however, was the demonstration of the staff's trust in the aides' capacity to grow, learn, and to be adequate to the task. If the staff was willing to invest this much time and energy in their capacity, then perhaps their own inner fears of inadequacy were not so real.

During these initial stages the aides were involved in all the planning and policy making for the project. To some extent such extension of authority evolved to an overly democratic situation in which all people were involved in all decisions at all times. The aides, however, found participation in decision making to their liking because it enabled them to allay some of their anxieties; although the situation was chaotic, they usually knew what was going on and each of them had the opportunity to affect its outcome. Because they did have an influence, because their suggestions, objections, and concerns were acted upon, and above all, frequently incorporated into project policies and procedures, their sense of self-esteem was enhanced.

In their relationship to patients, as stated previously, the aides frequently felt very inadequate to affect the patient in any way. This pessimism was usually voiced in descriptions of the patients as "hopeless." The staff offered support here by suggesting possible alternative ways of coping with the patient's behavior, by trying to help the aides get more understanding and perspective regarding the patient, and by pointing out and reacting to progress in the patient, especially when the manifestations of that progress were subtle.

The initial efforts of the project staff to protect the aides from the consequences of some of their behavior were also found to be supportive. There were many occasions initially when errors in judgment on the part of the aides were justified to other hospital staff members by the project staff, or the project staff would request that reactions or the disciplinary action be held in abeyance, at least temporarily. The aides tended to interpret this kind of behavior on the part of the project staff as one in which they too were "laying their jobs on the line" and fully sharing with the aides the risks, whether fantasied or real, in the project.

Whenever the tentative relationship with the project staff was in any way disrupted by them, it was usually a project staff member who made the first move to reestablish the relationship; it was the project staff who went out after the aides; it was the project staff who saw it as their primary responsibility to reestablish the relationship and clear up any problems. Finally, what was perhaps most helpful to the aides was the respect for their personal style and spontaneity. Their humor, relaxed approach to patients, and down-to-earth ways of expressing themselves were stimulating and pleasurable to the project staff. This mutual respect served as the basis for the development of close personal relationships among project members.

Conclusions—First Phase

During these first few months of the project the aides and the project staff were too immersed in their own problems and concerns to involve themselves in any detailed or systematic way with the patients. Throughout this period the major concern, especially of the aides, was the experience of the new role, i.e., the proper use of their new authority and the establishment of this authority as a reality. In retrospect it became obvious that this was a great change for the aides. True, they were certainly used to authority and responsibility in their personal lives at home with their children, but they were not used to being perceived in this way in the hospital. It has also become clear that the hospital's social structure and administrative system, in and of itself, did a great deal to structure the aides in their previous role. To give the aides a new role was to interrupt the old attitudes. Consequently, some of the old traditions, the old patterns of habits were detrimental to the formation of this new role in the aides and had to be changed. Inevitably the development of this new role took time; it needed to be tested experimentally and behaviorally. There would be some emotional turbulence, not only on the part of the project aides and staff, but also in those other members of the hospital staff who related to the aides, as well as the patients and the community. The staff was also in the process of learning, and they too had problems fulfilling their roles in a consistent manner. It was difficult for the aides to maintain a model of consistent behavior and a firm structure for their patients when their own models were changing. The aides' overreaction to staff may have been in part a protest against just such shifting sands. It became apparent that a great deal of support would be needed if the aides were eventually to evolve into this new role.

Again in retrospect, it would appear that the support offered to the aides was primarily in terms of a new model of behavior, a model that was, on the one hand, relatively in harmony with their own personal style, but on the other consistent with the treatment theory. The staff responded to the aides in much the same way that the aides were expected to respond to the patients. The staff was intrusive and active and attempted to solve real problems. Introspection and verbalism were deemphasized, self-experience and self-experimentation were strongly encouraged. There was a great emphasis on the communication of trust and personal respect for the aides, as well as an expectation of a higher level of performance and re-

sponsibility because of faith in their competence. Failure
and error were tolerated as essential aspects of the growth
process.

Thus in these first months everyone was full of much
open enthusiasm and many secret fears. The lack of
precedents increased natural feelings of insecurity; there
was a constant expectation of catastrophe around every
corner. Talking only made the situation worse. To demonstrate that whatever came along could be accepted and
dealt with successfully was crucial.

PHASE TWO—THE NEXT FIVE MONTHS

By October 1960 subtle changes were observed in the
aides. With the passage of time, changes in self-esteem
were noticed. Some of these changes were more obvious,
others more subtle. Because the aides had explored the
limits of their roles in relationship with the staff, the need
for testing was reduced; these boundaries had gradually
become internalized with concomitant changes in behavior and judgment.

Where earlier they had appeared to be more concerned
with the authority invested in them, the aides were now
becoming more aware of the other side of this coin, that
is, responsibility. Their meaning and importance to the
patients loomed large in their minds. This new identity
as a significant agent for change in the life of the patient
emerged gradually, rather than in a rapid or dramatic
fashion. On the surface their behavior was much the
same; to some extent the more aware they were of their
responsibilities and their importance to the patient, the
more they became anxious and frightened. Despite their
anxiety, however, there was an intensification of their efforts at relating to the patient in a close, meaningful, and
goal-directed fashion.

Development of Aide-Patient Relationship

Observers saw for the first time an aide behaving as
though her relationship with the patient meant something. The patients were becoming persons for the aides.
More aware now of the patients' unique and characteristic
reactions to various kinds of stresses, they were able to re-

port not only negative behavior but also positive improvement. They began to like their patients. They seemed more able to put themselves into the patient's shoes and understand her feelings, at times, in a dramatic way.

Betty, a member of Mrs. Jones' group, was noted for her loud, obstreperous and rude behavior. One morning Mrs. Jones' group had asked if it would be possible for them to go downtown as a group and window shop and roam around. Mrs. Jones felt this was an excellent idea and encouraged them to do so. As the patients were dressing and preparing for the trip downtown, Betty began to behave in an excessively domineering, loud and rude way with the other patients. At this point, the patients approached Mrs. Jones and indicated that they did not want to take Betty because "she did not know how to behave with others." Mrs. Jones discussed this with them for a while and finally agreed to let the group go downtown without Betty. After the group left, she and Betty sat down to talk about the incident. At this point Betty began to talk about herself in a self-derogatory way, communicating her self-hatred and her deep hurt at being rejected by the other patients. As she talked of this she began to cry and very soon thereafter Mrs. Jones began to cry also. She told Betty that she was aware of how much it did hurt her, but that the patients did have a point and that she and Betty would both have to work on helping her to learn to "behave better."

As they were able to empathize with the patients' pain, so too they were more able to empathize with the patients' experience of pleasure.

Mrs. Watts and Mrs. Wash took their group of patients out to a summer cabin on one of the nearby lakes for a weekend. The cabin was owned by the parents of one of the patients in the group. The group had an enjoyable time boating, picnicing, hiking through the woods, etc. However, one of the patients in the group, Margaret, who had always been a good swimmer, asked a number of times if she could go swimming in the lake. Since neither Mrs. Watts nor Mrs. Wash could swim they were reluctant to let her do this and denied her the request. As the group was preparing to go back to the hospital at the end of the weekend, Margaret suddenly broke away from the group, ran out onto the dock, stripped off her clothes, and jumped into the lake. In rapid strokes she swam out to a raft and climbed onto it, stood there smiling in her naked glory and then dove into the water once more, swimming back to the dock. While this was happening Mrs. Wash walked out onto the dock, sat down and watched Margaret. As she came walking out of the water onto the shore Mrs. Wash met her and said, "It was fun, wasn't it." Margaret indicated that it had been and Mrs. Wash said, "We will have to arrange for you to swim more frequently." In reporting the incident later Mrs. Wash glowed with pleasure as she described how immensely satisfying the experience had been for Margaret.

As their capacity for empathy increased, so did their degree of involvement with patients. In many ways they were able to get closer and more perceptive; the patient took on increasing importance to them as a person, not merely as an object remanded to their care.

Barbara was a very frightening patient, in part because she seemed to have the capacity deliberately to go out of contact. She would pace up and down the hall, her eyes staring blankly, cursing, crying, talking about being lost and making wild statements such as "Even that damn God is out of reality." When she came out of her "spell" with no warning she would engage in assaultive or suicidal behavior. Because she was so withdrawn in between attacks, the staff was never really able to predict when such acts might occur. This part of Barbara's behavior had a highly unsettling effect on most of the people around her. But there was another aspect to this patient; the perceptive observer could see in her a great deal of inner turmoil and strain, much pain, a deep sense of hopelessness, a feeling that she could never recover or that even if she did, it would not be worthwhile, that she was much too destructive and would never be able to control herself.

For some months her aide, Mrs. Douglas, in daily meetings with the staff would repeat that she was a hopeless case, that there was nothing she could really do for this patient. Even though Mrs. Douglas was a fairly even-tempered person, albeit with a dash of cynicism in her philosophy of life, the situation depressed her. She felt terribly frustrated; she felt unable to get through Barbara's shell which had never been cracked by anyone. And at other times she would be overwhelmed by the inner pain Barbara seemed to be experiencing.

The staff at first tried to convince Mrs. Douglas that Barbara was not hopeless. Eventually the team suggested that if she felt so strongly about it, she ought to tell Barbara. The next time Barbara went into a very despairing phase, Mrs. Douglas took her aside and told Barbara that she thought she was hopeless. Mrs. Douglas went on to state that she personally did not know whether Barbara was hopeless, but whether she would leave the hopsital or not was inconsequential. The essential point was not to worry about the hopelessness; Mrs. Douglas was there, she was concerned about her, and Barbara could at least relate to her and get along. They could try to do things together that might make daily life a little less painful for Barbara and might even have a little bit of fun.

From that time on, there was a dramatic change in Barbara. She began to let Mrs. Douglas become important to her; the shell began to crack a little and there was less assaultiveness and severe self-destructiveness. The old Barbara might reappear on occasion when Mrs. Douglas had not dealt successfully with some problem, but at least there seemed to have been a tremendous release of tension between the two. The plan was now one of living from day to day, taking care of the little details of each day but avoiding an "overall life plan."

Barbara's improvement never went much beyond a good adjustment to hospital living, but she became a much safer and easier patient to work with. A few months after this incident the patients held a Spring Sing on the ward. They invited a group of personnel and staff as guests. Barbara acted as hostess; she would meet people at the door, hand them the printed program, and seat them. She did an excellent job. There was still that kind of shell about her, but there was such appropriateness in her behavior that the staff was quite surprised.

Now the aides also became much more protective of their patients and began to go into "battle" for them. Many patients had never had anyone to care deeply for them. Since the aides were very much aware of the "underdog" status of the patients, they were extremely protective of them. They would become quite angry when the beauty shop "hadn't fixed the patient's hair right," when the pharmacy didn't have the "right kind of medication," or when a relative who had promised to visit did not come. At this point the aides were annoyed because others did not care for the patients or had not cooperated in doing everything possible for them. Almost without exception the aides' attitude toward the "offending party" was a hostile one, especially when this person was a relative.

As they empathized more with their patients and became more involved and protective, there was also greater identification with them. The patients' living quarters began to concern them; they felt the ward was unattractive and lacking in cheer. At this time there was increased urgency about making the ward more attractive and comfortable for the patients. Because of a need for money to make these improvements the aides began to use previously granted permission to engage in money-making activities with the patients. The funds derived from these activities were then used to buy knick-knacks, rugs, and furniture to refurbish the ward.

The aides now became much more solicitous about the patients' appearance; patients were supervised more closely in dressing and personal care. The volunteer services of the hospital were utilized to obtain better clothing for patients unable to afford it; through the services of a volunteer a "charm class" was started to help the more intact patients learn to dress better and improve their appearance. The aides tried to make the daily activities of the patients more stimulating because they were felt to be humdrum, unappealing, and downright boring. New activities were designed; more patients were assigned to industrial therapy; more passes were given to leave the ward, either individually or in groups; cooking classes were begun; coffee hours were initiated as well as a weekly ward social on Sunday evenings that included men from other parts of the hospital.

However, the increasing involvement and identification with the patients had its negative aspects. There still was a great deal of evidence that many of the aides needed to prove their capacity and worth through the patients. When patients would regress or would not make progress, the aides frequently tended to feel personally responsible; they would become annoyed, and at times saddened by the patients' lack of appreciation for their efforts. It was as though they felt the patient owed it to them to get well.

In this overidentification the aides frequently became possessive. Whenever another aide had to relieve them, they would criticize her methods with their patients. They became competitive, and were reluctant to share their growth and experiences with one another. They frequently commented upon each other's personal style in derogatory fashion.

Perhaps nowhere was the strong identification with the patient more apparent than in the relationship with the families. There were the inevitable conflicts with families about patients. Relationships between the aides and the ward social worker were not yet good enough so that these conflicts could be forestalled, and in such battles the patient was often the loser. The aides were dimly aware of this dilemma, but they seemed powerless to act differently. Since the aides saw the patients as vulnerable creatures given them to help, anything that seemed to impede their development would be attacked and in such striking out, since it was "just," much anger and tension could be released. If Mary's mother was a psychotic old harridan who caused Mary so much trouble, then one could hate that mother and be less annoyed at her fellow aides, at a difficult situation, or at Mary who frequently might be intensely irritating.

Despite the high level of anxiety in the aides, despite the negative features of their identification with the patient, their increased involvement and empathy began to bring results. They began to see changes for the better in their patients. In the extremely chronic and regressed patients the alterations would be rudimentary, subtle, but definite. In their more intact patients, changes were sometimes even dramatic.

Each change was met with jubilation by the staff, but not always so by the aides. Such changes in the patients did tend to alleviate some of their anxiety and self-doubt; but, on the other hand, if it were they who brought about the changes, then their responsibility toward the patient would be even more awesome.

Development of Aide-Staff Relationship

The growth in the aides was apparent, not only in their relationship to the patients, but also in their relationship to the project staff. It was evident they were beginning to feel more secure with the staff; they increasingly were coming to feel protected and accepted. The character of their relationship to the staff began to go through subtle changes. The aides did not need to involve themselves in all planning. They were able to see that some aspects of the project were basically irrelevant to their work or outside their area of competence; and they merely required feedback on what was occurring in these areas when it related to them or when they simply wanted to know what was going on in general. Within the meetings there was less concern with the relationship between staff and aides and more of a task orientation. As their own roles began to emerge, their expectations of the staff became more clear.

As the aides felt more secure, they began to relate by means of the deeper, more personal aspects of themselves. It was at this time that they would openly discuss race with the staff; generally this discussion would be in the context of one of the patient's, or a patient's relative's, reaction to the fact that the aide was Negro. This might be followed with the question of how to cope with such attitudes.

As a consequence of their security with the staff, the aides manifested an increased independence from them. In January 1960, when both project directors were away from the hospital for a period of three weeks, the aides did not become overly anxious. Upon the directors' return, the aides took a great deal of pride in their self-sufficiency and in the fact that no serious "mistakes" or crises had occurred.

Another aspect of the increasing independence was that unprecedented activities or decisions began to be undertaken without prior discussion with the project staff.

The project directors arrived on the ward on Monday to meet with the aides to discuss their patients. During the hour the aides discussed nearly all their patients but omitted any discussion of Aleda whom they had been working with quite intensively for some time. Near the end of the consultation hour one of the directors asked, "What about Aleda?" Mrs. Stillman responded, "She's no longer here." Both of the directors were surprised and asked where she was. Mrs. Stillman went on to indicate that she had been placed in a nursing home over the weekend. She said that the nursing home was located near her home, that she knew the nursing home operator and had discussed with her the placement of Aleda. She went on to indicate that Aleda would be able to both work and live in the nursing home and would draw a salary. They had decided over the weekend to go ahead and place her. Both of the directors were momentarily taken aback but then went on to indicate that they were pleased with Mrs. Stillman's initiative.

As the aides gained confidence, they became increasingly willing to disagree with the project staff and with their consultants. They seemed to enjoy being able to disagree, and there were times when the consultants felt that the only reason they were requesting advice was the opportunity it presented for contradiction.

A further consequence of their security was increased autonomy of functioning. As indicated above, they were initiating more activities, they were making unprecedented decisions, they were more able to disagree with the project staff. In addition, they were also becoming less dependent upon the traditional support system utilized by the nursing service in the hospital. Each section had a section charge aide for each shift. In the past this person has usually functioned as a "grievance board" for aides. It was this person aides talked to whenever they had complaints about nurses, other aides, doctors, etc. It was this person they usually looked to for protection and support. The afternoon shift on the project had previously appeared more comfortable when the afternoon charge aide sat in on their meetings with the staff. However, it became apparent about this time that this need no longer prevailed. The section charge aide sensed that she was no longer needed in this capacity and was able to withdraw from these meetings.

The increasing autonomy also had its consequences in the relationship of the partner aides to each other. Just as they had become more independent from the project staff and their supervisors, so too with their fellow aides they were becoming more autonomous. However, as one of the goals of the project was to provide a consistent attitude and approach to the patient, preserving this consistency provoked problems. At times one of the aides would begin to feel that her partner was not cooperating or was functioning in a manner inconsistent with the way she functioned, or that through her behavior her partner was sabotaging her efforts with the patients. This problem was discussed for some time. Obviously the project would have to differentiate more clearly what it meant by consistency. Through discussion there developed a general consensus that consistency referred to goals. *Agreement was essential on the goals for the patient, but each aide must be free to use her own personal style in implementing these goals.* From these discussions a norm evolved that was to assume increasing importance throughout the life of the project. Goal setting was a mutual interdependent function, but each person was free to utilize his own means and style to attain those goals. A person was to be held accountable for results, that is, goal achievement, but not for means. From these discussions two norms evolved governing interactions between aides that continued to have validity throughout the life of the project. One aide could not tell her partner how to behave toward a patient—they both must agree on goals for that patient. They were to keep each other informed what had happened during the off shift.

Broadening Horizons

As the new approaches and formulations suggested to the aides by the consultants and the ward staff began to have the desired results, the aides developed interest in learning more. Further, the frustration engendered by the lack of progress on the part of some of their patients frequently precipitated a loss of their still rather fragile self-esteem. Previously the aides were quick to believe that the lack of improvement by these patients reflected their own inadequacy, despite the fact that these patients had shown little improvement over many years of treatment. However, the successes they now had led them to approach problems differently this time. In the past where such problems had been handled by scapegoating or other crisis-producing externalizations, now they became increasingly concerned with learning new approaches and developing their competence. In their meetings with the ward staff they were more interested in using the time to describe their problems with patients, to explore what was going on in the patient, and to outline possible alternative ways of coping with problems. Their request now was that the staff share their competence with them. This impetus toward learning was also evident in their use of the consultants; the aides became increasingly ingenious in presenting patient problems to the consultants and using their help in arriving at solutions. On occasion the aides asked to consult with aides in other areas of the hospital who had had similar experience with patients. Along with this growth in the aides' ability there was increased sophistication on the part of staff and consultants in their meaningful interaction with the aides.

Further, the aides' orientation to patients in the project did not remain static. During this period one aide stopped the project director and told him she was reading a book which had given her a new idea for the project. He was surprised because most of the aides drew their treatment ideas from personal experience. The aides began to demonstrate a great deal of interest in reports of similar projects and during these months made two trips to nearby hospitals to observe programs in which aides had an active role. In ward meetings they compared what they had observed elsewhere with their own program. They used these discussions to gain a more thorough understanding of what they were doing and also to change some of their own activities and approaches to patients.

With the aides' increased security, they began to broaden their horizons beyond the ward. This expanded interest was demonstrated in part by their increased contact with the patient's family; they talked more with relatives in an effort to get more understanding concerning the patient's previous life experiences and to explain the patient's problems more clearly to the family. Evidently the aides were attempting to have a persuasive effect on relatives. As indicated above, although this interaction between aides and families sometimes caused conflict, it also helped the aides to appreciate more deeply the abilities of the ward social worker. The aides began to make more use of the social worker in working out problems with families and in trying to understand the dynamics of family life. During this period a patient returned from her visit home visibly upset and filled with detailed stories about the bad treatment she had received there. Her aide did not feel too convinced by the patient's story and in her discussions with the ward staff she decided to make a home visit. She did so and saw at once that the stories were delusional. When she confronted the patient with this fact, they were able to discuss some long-standing problems in the patient's relationship to her family. As a result, the patient's subsequent visits home were more successful. The utilization of these experiences enabled the aides to continue working with families despite the conflict and frustration frequently encountered and despite their own generally negative feelings toward families.

Their broadened range of contacts included not only families but the remainder of the hospital and the community as well. In their money-making projects, e.g., selling cookies and preparing dinners for hospital personnel, they furthered their contact with the personnel of the hospital. The frequency with which aides took their patients to shop in downtown Topeka and to attend movies or recreational events increased, and they became increasingly competent in interpreting their activities to the community at large and in helping their patients make use of community facilities.

During the spring of the first year of the project one of the aides and the ward nurse had taken the aide's group of patients to a local park. While at the park they had an opportunity to chat with a worker at one of the city's recreation centers located in the park. The recreation leader indicated that during the winter the recreation center was relatively unused. They discussed the possibility of using the center for their patients. The recreation leader not only concurred but seemed enthusiastic; and the following week a series of meetings were held on the ward where the aides discussed what sort of therapeutic benefit such a program might be and which patients could best utilize it. They felt that a program in which both male and female patients could participate would be most useful. They thereupon contacted one of the male sections of the hospital, discussed the proposal with them, and made arrangements to take approximately eight patients from Ward H, as well as eight male patients from the male section, over to the park each week. The aides were enthusiastic about this venture and felt that socialization experiences as well as getting away from the hospital were extremely useful to the patients. After each trip to the center when the aides would return they would all gather together in the office and discuss what had happened. The aides who had accompanied the patients would fill in the other aides on what had happened with their patients. They felt that it provided an opportunity for them to make the kinds of observations that would not have been available to them at the hospital. They seemed to be concerned about the patients' social skills and their patients' attitudes toward themselves as women. During the week they again did a great deal of work with their patients in these areas and spent time talking with their patients in terms of their behavior around men.

Conclusions

By February of 1961, the project directors were able to report:

Some interesting personal changes in the aides have been noted. First of all, there has been an increase in the aides' independence and initiative; as they have become more deeply aware of their patients, as they have gotten to know them, there are times when they feel that an activity needs to be instituted with the patient, or a certain course of action taken. At this point they institute these procedures. We have also seen an increase in the degree of spontaneity in the aides' daily behavior. They are usually quite active in their meetings. They are very forthright in their opinions, easily express their feelings, and readily enter into and lead discussions about the ward, the project, and the patients.

Lastly, there has been a marked increase in the degree of involvement they have with their patients. They feel very much identified with them, and also feel they have something at stake in the patients' improvement. There are negative aspects to these developments; one of the more obvious is the aides' frequent expectation that the patient owes it to them to get well. As a result, if the patient happens to regress or have a bad week, the aides are prone to get angry with the patient over this backsliding. Again, support becomes vitally necessary here; if they happen to have someone there to knock the edge off their frustration, to reassure them or to help them understand why this happened to the patient and what possible courses of action can be taken, this disappointment need not interfere with the treatment of the patient.

While the changes described above were not yet stable, there was striking evidence that the aides had made several giant strides in the development of their new role. They demonstrated a growing sense of responsibility through their increasingly frequent constructive participation in structuring the immediate environment toward the more efficient achievement of their task. Through dialogue with the staff they precipitated changes in the meeting structure, helped to delineate project responsibility, and evolve patterns and norms for governing their working relationship among themselves. They demonstrated an increasing capacity to recognize and utilize the resources available to them. They were becoming more able to ask for help and take suggestions without feeling they were giving up their authority and responsibility. They were demonstrating increasing involvement with their patients and were showing their concern through more discriminating goal-setting and empathic identification.

PHASE THREE—THE NEXT FOUR MONTHS

Thus in the latter part of the first year the project had indeed entered a new phase. The earlier problems of the aides had come to a resolution; the essence of this resolution was the adaptation of the aides to their new role. They had developed the capacity for responsible functioning, not only in their attitude toward the patients, but also toward themselves and the staff. While they still lacked much in terms of competence, their feelings about themselves had changed. Therefore the staff felt confident that the work of the preceding eight months had come to fruition. Certainly the questions concerning the aides' competence would take a great deal more time; only experience and further training could bring about increased ability; but the essential attitudes toward themselves and toward responsible functioning had been developed.

It was apparent that these aides were experiencing themselves in a new way. They now had little doubt about their capacity to bring about change. Physically the ward had changed a great deal. There was much bric-a-brac about, which the patients not only tolerated but seemed

to like. Incidents of assault had decreased and there was
evidence of increased sociability among patients, e.g.,
they frequently talked among themselves, they talked to
visitors, and they talked a great deal to the aides. The
aides felt they were more able to predict what patients
would do under given circumstances and they seemed
more comfortable about their capacity to handle situations in a useful way. They also saw that patients were
beginning in subtle ways to identify with the aides. Many
patients copied the aides' manner of speech; others began
imitating the behavior of the aides in their relations with
other patients. Consequently, the aides were left with the
conviction that relating closely and intensely with patients
could bring about change; they were hopeful that the
change would be in the direction of improvement for patients.

Perhaps even more important, the aides found that they
were enjoying their work and actually were finding it immensely satisfying. And now they would frequently sit
and contrast the old with the new ways of working with
patients. As one aide said, "In the old days you selected
one or two patients from the ward that you liked and
cared about, and you let the rest go. Whenever you had
to deal with something that you didn't want to, you
passed the buck to the doctor, but basically there were
only one or two patients that you cared about. The rest
of them you knew were pretty much out from under your
control, that it depended a great deal upon how the doctor saw it, and you couldn't do anything about it anyway, so you simply didn't care. Now it is different. You
have nine patients; it's all up to you; you care about all
nine of them, and while it is scary and lots of work, you
know that if you want to do something with them you
can, and you know that if they do improve it is because
you tried to help them."

Thus they were committed to the project and to the
new role that had been created for them and that they
had accepted. Their one major concern was how long the
project would last. They had invested a great deal of
energy and effort in the project; they had identified with
it and had accepted its new role for them. When the
project grant was accepted for National Institute of Men-

tal Health support in the summer of 1961, the aides were
extremely gratified; now they had assurance that at least
for the time being they could continue with their new
role.

Most important to the project staff was that the growth
in the aides' attitude implied a more realistic set of expectations. Certainly this more realistic approach characterized their relationship with patients; the aides seldom felt now that patients were hopeless, and they did
not now believe that they had to be experts or had to
have experts immediately available in order to benefit
the patients. Rather, they began to see patient improvement as a function of the interpersonal relationship that
pertained between them and the patients, and they saw
that for most of their patients this growth would be a
long-term affair, with changes coming about slowly. At
this point, most of their planning was long-range. They
were concerned about setting up a structure for the patients through the use of their own personalities and, in
effect, letting this structure have its effect on the patients
over a long time.

That their expectations were increasingly realistic was
made evident in their relationship with the staff. They
were more accepting of staff support, both in an emotional and cognitive sense. They could accept the staff
empathizing with them and with their problems, the
staff's efforts to help them work out their own feelings,
and the staff's conviction that they as aides could do well.
But they also were able to accept support by availing
themselves of the staff's competence and knowledge about
psychopathology and the treatment process. They were
very much concerned about learning more theory, but
learning it in their terms. They were not familiar nor at
home with much of the professional jargon used by the
staff, and slowly over the months the language of psycho-
pathological and treatment theory began to evolve in the
aides' terms.

As well as being able to recognize and accept their
need for support from the staff, they also were able to see
that the staff needed support from them. At this point
one of the aides talked to a resident psychiatrist with
whom she had worked previously. As they talked about

the project and the roles of the various people involved, the aide became aware of the psychiatrist's anxiety over the project's impact on the role of the doctor and how difficult it must be for doctors to work in this new kind of role. In one of the ward meetings she reported this conversation; a discussion followed concerning the problems of not only the aides with their roles, but the supporting staff as well. The aides seemed much more sensitive to the staff's worries and were now able to see the staff as "real" people who had their problems with the project, who could not do magic, who did not always know all the answers. Finally, they began to see how the staff had to rely to a great extent on the aides to point out where their energies were needed.

The aides began to report their own needs much more succinctly and clearly, and this in turn enabled the staff to respond more adequately to these needs. One of the problems brought up at this time concerned the meeting structure, which did not really promote the kind of consultation with the staff that the aides needed. Until this time, all the aides on a given shift met every day with members of the staff and talked about psychopathology and patient problems. This daily conference had been useful for a time but now no longer was because each aide wanted to talk about her own patients. In addition, there was now an increased need for coordination between the two partner aides, the one on the morning, and the one on the afternoon shift. After a series of discussions, both the staff and the aides agreed to hold what came to be called "partner" meetings. Each partner pair met together once a week with the ward staff to discuss their nine patients. The staff was now able to help them more adequately in evolving a program that was consistent and coordinated between the two partners; they were able to assist in working out the inevitable conflicts over the use of personal style. Further, they were able to maintain a continuous consultative contact with the aides that was related specifically to their work with patients.

Just as the aides demonstrated more realism in their attitude toward patients and staff, they also appraised themselves more objectively. They no longer expected themselves to bring about magical changes based upon a single interpersonal interaction in patients; they no longer felt that they needed to know everything in order to relate to the patient, but they felt the chances were good that with staff support the use of their personal style could bring about improvement in the patient. In any case, they no longer seemed to feel the intense need to prove themselves; rather, they seemed to relax and feel that their relating to the patient in a way consistent with the treatment theory would slowly, over a long time, bring about the improvement in which they were all deeply interested.

UNRESOLVED AND RESIDUAL PROBLEMS
OF THE FIRST YEAR

At the end of the first year of the project the ward was functioning well. The patients were making progress, the ward was a beehive of activities, and those associated with the project had much to be proud of. However, a series of problems had been growing and developing.

The first of these problems was related in a general way to the competence of the aides. They had taken on new responsibilities well, their attitude toward what they were doing was good, but in some areas the aides' competence was not adequate. It became clear that the past year's training and experience in the project had not provided them with certain skills necessary for their task. For example, the aides were not adequately trained to consider their interactions with patients in process terms. Frequently they would become enmeshed in a single event, a single interaction with a patient, and would have difficulty in gaining perspective on the meaning of this particular event in the whole process of the patient's treatment. They were also having difficulty generalizing from this event to the patient's total program and goals. The directors had believed that this amount of time and experience would be sufficient to allow the aides to develop the necessary perspective and ability. However, this had been an overoptimistic hope. The aides had not been given an adequate theoretical framework to use in understanding this aspect of their work.

This lack was becoming more evident by the end of the year; the need for its solution was now apparent.

This same problem had another aspect related to the development of innovations in the treatment program and goal setting. Again, the aides' lack of theoretical framework hampered them in setting goals for patients and in developing innovations for themselves that would be consistent with their attempts to relate meaningfully with patients. This problem became evident when the staff found itself frequently compelled to establish for the aides new goals for their patients. This staff interference, necessary as it was at the time, set up a real contradiction in the aims of the project. On the one hand, the aides had been given the authority and responsibility to deal with their particular charges; on the other, this new independence was vitiated by having the staff set goals and initiate innovations. Above all, a real dilemma could be created for the aides by the inconsistency of supposedly giving them responsibility and authority while in reality retaining goal-setting as a prerogative of the staff. However, lacking a conceptual basis for making innovations, the aides had a tendency to founder and continue beyond their appropriate time specific treatments with specific patients. The problem of the staff helping the aides to innovate and to set goals without usurping their authority and responsibility became central. The nuances of this problem and the lack of clarity about it for the professional staff only served to confuse the aides.

At this time there also developed a new series of crises. Earlier in the year the anxiety the aides had about their new-found authority had been evident in a continuing series of crises. By the end of the year, however, this anxiety had been dealt with. Now, however, anxiety became evident in the supporting professional staff and manifested itself in several crises and withdrawals from the ward. It became evident that the social service, adjunctive therapy, and nursing departments were withdrawing in part their investment in the program. A supervising nurse who had contact with the program told the project directors that she could intellectually appreciate what was being done and thought that it was worthwhile, but personally could not participate in it because of its discrepancy with her background and training. The ward nurse who had been with the project since the very beginning quit quite suddenly. The problem of the supervising nurse's withdrawal and the ward nurse's resignation were the first concrete difficulties the project had encountered over the role of the registered nurse in this kind of program, a problem that was to become most difficult for the project to resolve. It was difficult to pinpoint the source of these anxieties in the professional staff; evidently there was an ill-defined frustration present throughout this group which precipitated these withdrawals and needed to be attended to without delay.

Another major area of problems at this time centered around the relationships between the project and the rest of the hospital. When the project had first been presented to the hospital staff it had been received very warmly and enthusiastically. Now, after a year, the enthusiasm had waned considerably and there was a discrepancy between the current attitude of the hospital toward the project and the initial one. The project seemed to be serving as an irritant in the daily operation of the hospital and co-operation was increasingly difficult between the various departments in the institution and the project itself. One of the activities the aides and patients had wanted to perform was the painting of the ward; this project caused conflict with the painters in the maintenance section of the hospital. The business office had difficulty in dealing with the unusual work orders from the ward and there was a series of problems over payment which patients and relatives owed for hospitalization.

Probably the most obvious difficulty in the relations with the hospital came over the project's contact with the clinical services. Thus, for example, it took nine months to replace the nurse who had quit on the ward. Concern was expressed by the medical personnel of the institution; they wondered how medical responsibility could be kept intact when in reality the physician assigned to the ward had no personal contact with the patients who were his legal charge. How could the doctor be held responsible for what happened to his patients when he was not able to see them?

These four areas then became the focus of concern for the project at the end of the first year. The work was alive and vital in the day-to-day interactions between the patients and the aides, but solutions were urgently needed for these other critical problems to maintain this life and allow for the continuing development of the program as a whole.

5

The Second Year

At the end of the first year there was an ill-defined sense of frustration and anxiety among the project staff. The project directors were concerned with the ultimate effect of this vague anxiety on the aides and their patients, and upon the project's viability within the hospital. Certainly many of the hospital staff members' attitudes had grown increasingly negative toward the project. In addition, observers had reported that since the resignation of the ward nurse treatment activity on the ward had decreased; one found patients sitting idle much more frequently than before, and the aides showed less interest in initiating new programs.

The resignation of the nurse had precipitated a major crisis on the ward. In discussions with the project directors and her supervisors she seemed unable to articulate her reasons for resigning with any degree of clarity; all that she could indicate was her increasing frustration and diminished satisfaction with her work. Some of her observations and the observations of others did lend credence to the notion that much of her difficulty may have arisen out of the administrative structure of the project. Certainly she did have a complex role, in reality a mixture of two or three different and partially incompatible roles: she was a part of the ward team as well as part of the research team; she was a ward supervisor as well as a consultant to the aides; she was also responsible for the teaching of technique to the aides.

In addition to the multiplicity of role expectations a second complication was a concomitant multiplicity of supervisory contacts; the ward nurse had supervisory relationships with the chief nurse of the section, the assistant director of nursing service, the ward physician, and the project directors, each of whom had inconsistent and incompatible expectations of her.

Dr. Reyes, the ward physician, also found herself in a difficult position. After adapting to her role as a consultant to the aides, she found her work immensely gratifying. When in July of this year she began to supervise three first-year psychiatric residents in the Topeka State Hospital residency training program, she decided she would like to have them participate in the project. Consequently, each of the residents was assigned to one of the aide partner groups. Initially each resident was to be there as an observer and gradually was to assume Dr. Reyes' consultant role vis-à-vis the aides to which he had been assigned. It soon became evident that the residents did not find the role of consultant particularly satisfying and on occasions voiced their discontent to Dr. Reyes. In addition, Dr. Reyes found little support among her psychiatric colleagues who expressed to her many of their concerns about legal responsibility for the patients.

The project directors were very anxious and concerned about maintaining the integrity of the project. They were worried about the inability of the aides to think of their patients in process terms and to set their own goals for patients. Although cognizant of the discontent among the supporting staff, the directors were perplexed about its remedy. They also became aware that the "honeymoon" between the hospital and the project was over. They felt that the remainder of the hospital now saw the project as sufficiently stable and secure to tolerate critical questioning; in general, they felt that this kind of questioning would be beneficial in furthering the development and growth of the project as well as an articulation of the project's structure, goals, methods, and processes. However, they were anxious to prevent hospital criticism from having a deleterious effect upon the morale of the project staff and the aides.

Certainly these concerns were not an exhaustive list; the social worker and the adjunctive therapist connected with the project also had their concerns, but they were even more vaguely expressed.

In an effort to get some clarification of the sources of the rather ill-defined anxieties among the supporting staff, the project directors decided to call in outside consultants. Since there had been some indications that problems existed in the social organization of the project and in the relationship of the project group to the remainder of the hospital, the project directors approached Dr. William Key, a sociologist, for consultation. He was asked to evaluate what was happening on the ward, the nature of the interpersonal relationships there, the effects of these factors on the project, and how these factors influenced the project's relationship to the hospital. He was free to observe wherever he felt necessary and to interview anyone whose opinions and attitudes might in his opinion be relevant. Dr. Key spent approximately one month interviewing and observing most of the people involved in the project, as well as crucial members of the hospital staff.

In his report to the project directors Dr. Key pointed out that in focusing on the aides the project neglected to define the roles of the other ward personnel and to train them in the skills necessary for the maintenance of those roles. Rather, the project directors had assumed these roles. Dr. Key pointed out that innovations oriented toward role changes within organizations were particularly unsettling and conflictual. He went on to indicate:

> Some conflict is to be expected as a result of any social change. The more rapid and extensive the change, the more basic the alteration of roles and the more intense the conflicts. This is especially true in psychiatric hospitals where there is no common agreement on what constitutes "therapy," the manifest function of the organization. The propriety of any activity is subject to question under the most stable of circumstances and each separate group feels called upon to defend its own rather insecure place in the hospital. It is rather easy to see how this project threatens to upset the status quo and motivates people to engage in defensive action.

Dr. Key pointed out that lack of provision for the role development of the supporting staff had failed to involve the various clinical departments of the hospital in the work of the project. The various disciplines were not communicating with the project, nor were others being trained to function in a compatible way. While the presence of the project directors might have been necessary earlier to set the structure of the project and to establish the norms governing the relationship of the supporting staff to the aides, these norm-setting interventions were no longer needed. Rather, the presence of the directors now left no room for the roles of the supporting staff to evolve and differentiate as had the roles of the aides. Not only had the project failed to specify roles for the supporting staff, but it was also neglecting the optimal conditions necessary for role development.

In addition it was pointed out that if the project's viability was to depend upon the presence of a single person or persons, institutionalization (the integration of the project into the total hospital structure) would not occur. Dr. Key indicated that if projects or change are more dependent on the personality of individuals than on the institutionalization of social roles within the structure of the organization, the changes will last only so long as those individuals are present. Finally, Dr. Key raised the issue of the competence of the aide staff and the nature of their relationship with the patients. His concerns and those of many others were stated succinctly by one of the ward observers who indicated:

> Concerning where the aides stand right now, it would appear to me that, all in all, they can do the patients a great deal of good, they can take responsibility, they can intrude. The question now is one of the quality of these intrusions and the limits of their therapeutic capacity. One of the aides' more generalized problems is a great deal of difficulty in approaching the patient in other than what seems to them to be a practical way. There is a great deal of overemphasis on practicality, and the patient has to behave so that he meets their definition of practical, rather than their behaving in such a manner that the patients' needs for intrusiveness and stability are met.

Dr. Key raised the question of whether an educational program might be provided to broaden the aides' cognitive horizons and perceptions of the treatment situation. Dr. Key's recommendations were:

(1) The elimination of multiple roles.

(2) The withdrawal of the project directors from the ward.

(3) Emphasis upon the development of the roles of the supporting staff and reinvolvement of their respective disciplines in this evolvement.

(4) Focusing upon the construction of an organizational system that both lent itself to the achievement of the goals of the project and would be compatible with the overall administrative structure of the hospital.

On the basis of Dr. Key's evaluation the project directors recognized two needs within the project: first, the aides had a growing need for a theoretical schema in order to utilize, evaluate, and appraise their work and progress with patients; second, there was a need for role clarification and development among the supporting staff and the construction of an organizational model within which to work.

However, there were complicating factors that made it difficult to attack the problems of the supporting staff. The project directors found themselves faced with the difficulty of promoting the evolvement of role and identity for the supporting staff, dealing with their anxiety, while at the same time maintaining the integrity of the project and avoiding cross purposes. In addition, the problem of role development was further complicated by the knowledge that Dr. Reyes' visa was soon to expire and she was to return to the Philippines. Also, there was no ready replacement for the ward nurse, nor was there to be one for some months. The use of first-year residents as consultants to the aides was not working out well. It did not seem possible for one who had not yet gained technical competence in the usual role of the psychiatrist to assume the role of consultant. Finally, the aides still lacked the capacity to understand and observe ongoing processes in their patients and to set goals compatible with those processes. To some extent many of these functions had to be performed by the consulting staff. The imminent loss of Dr. Reyes and the too-rapid withdrawal of the project directors would leave the aides without adequate support in this area. At best, during this year there could only be further evaluation, discussion, and careful planning of proposed solutions for these problems to be placed in effect the following year. This postponement of action permitted time and energy to be deployed in constructing with the aides a meaningful theoretical framework.

THEORETICAL SCHEMA

In view of the observations of Dr. Key and the project staff there was a new awareness of the need to help the aides gain perspective on their patients, to learn to think of them in process terms, to generalize, to establish goals, and to make innovations in the program in a manner consistent with the treatment theory and the project. It was necessary to make them less dependent upon practicality as the single criterion for judging patient behavior.

Obviously, the aides knew their patients; they were aware of their concrete behavior; they understood much of what worked with the patients and what did not. On the other hand, the project directors knew the theory and knew what aspects of the theory applied to the various processes going on in the patient. The chief task then of the project during this year was to coordinate this knowledge of both theory and patients and to articulate it so that the aides could relate sequences of behaviors and interactions to the theory and apply those aspects of the theory relevant to the patient's treatment at a particular time.

It was apparent that the aides were aware of a developmental continuum that underlay the behaviors they reported of their different patients. Even though all of the patients were chronic schizophrenics, the aides had come to experience them as different people: of some they expected little, protected them, did more for them; others were given more responsibility, dealt with more complexly and had more expected of them.

This notion of an underlying continuum was also a fundamental postulate in the theory of Austin DesLauriers. He had indicated that schizophrenia was essentially the product of defective ego organization and that ego organization can be tied to developmental levels. When the infant is born there is no stable frame of reference for his inner experiences. For the healthy adult individual the major stable referent is a subjective, physical experience of the ego, of the self; but this notion of "me" has not evolved in the infant. Slowly, however, through the use of sensory and motor equipment, the infant begins to differentiate himself from the rest of the world; and, as he grows older, he continues to make increasingly complex differentiations and integrations of his experience. The various natural functions and abilities he was born with and those that later develop get drawn into a coherent, adaptive system. Throughout maturation a series of differentiations and integration of experience take place on successively higher and more complex levels. This fact of different levels of functioning or of different levels of ego organization had been discerned by the aides in their experience with the patient. What remained to be done was to order these levels on a continuum, to specify them more discretely and discriminatingly, and to categorize the behaviors which were consistent with each level of functioning.

The fact that patients did function on different levels was emphasized on two occasions early in the project when the aides worked with acute schizophrenic patients. These were young married women who had children and relatively healthy backgrounds. The schizophrenic break which hospitalized them was in each case their first. When admitted to the ward they were quite regressed, demonstrating the muscular rigidity of the catatonic. Progress in working with these patients was rapid. The aides' response to the patients, the patients' response to the aides, and the ability to identify and work out problems were all radically different from what was demonstrated in work with the chronic cases.

Out of this interaction between project staff and aides emerged the concept of levels. In their discussions with the aides, the project directors were able to articulate five gross levels of ego organization, levels in which the patient succcessively established his identity first at a physical level, next at a psychological level, and finally at a social level.

Level I

Essentially out of contact with self at primitive body level. Not really aware of own physical body to greater or lesser degree of obviousness. May not know name, may not recognize self in mirror, will be either mute, withdrawn, apathetic, clinging, silly, babbling, inappropriate or extremely tense, "wild" looking, pacing, etc.

Seems generally to have no, or at best, a dim realization of who those about her are. Unable to provide for own basic needs. Without support and protection of hospital, would probably die or engage in seriously self-destructive behaviors.

Level II

Patient may have a dim awareness of self as a physical being. Generally able to recognize her aide and makes some (though usually psychotic) efforts at communicating needs and wants. Communications frequently autistic. Frequently one feels he has not "gotten through" to patient. Behavior is generally childish and illogical. Can take care of basic physical needs (eating, dressing, etc.), but only when the aide directs, motivates, and organizes these for the patient.

Level III

Patient is able to experience, be aware of, and take responsibility for most of her physiological feelings and needs. At the same time may, under stress in novel situations, or in highly complex situations, experience transient episodes of confused bodily feelings. Major difficulty, however, is in experiencing, taking responsibility for, and differentiating psychological feelings. Needs support of the hospital to keep self and life organized and to protect her from stimulus situations which are likely to bring about an overwhelming upsurge of feeling. Will be awkward, inept, uncomfortable, and possibly inappropriate in social situations, and in relating to others.

Level IV

Patient's major problem here is that of functioning as a social being, of carrying definite social responsibilities, of functioning cooperatively with others in work, recreational, and social situations, and of establishing a reasonably adequate sexual identity and the appropriate social and vocational skills. Mild regressions can be expected under stress at times. Needs definite help and experience in assuming complex social responsibilities.

Level V

Patient is able to function adequately as a social being, take responsibility and function in the community and at home without support of the hospital, although may require occasional emotional support of the aide.

While this description had been useful to the project directors in elaborating for themselves various developmental steps in the theory as it applied to chronic schizophrenics, it tended to be a statement much too abstract, relied too strongly on theoretical jargon and was inadequately specific about behaviors manifested by the patient. The task now lay in translating these abstract theories into terms meaningful and useful for the aides.

How this translation of theory into terms meaningful to the aides occurred was essentially that of a dialogue between the project directors, the project staff and the aides throughout the course of the second year of the project. Initially, the project directors began by attempting to explain and elaborate upon each of the five points or levels on the continuum of ego integration. During numerous meetings these five levels were discussed with the aides; once they had gained some basic understanding of each of the levels, further discussions were aimed at achieving a consensus among the aides and the project staff concerning which patients on the ward clearly exemplified these five levels. The discussions tried to describe these patients in terms of observed behavior, what could be done working with them, what could be expected of them, what the patients wanted from the aide. In effect, the levels and the patients were discussed in the framework of observable behaviors and aide-patient transactions.

For example, there was a general agreement that Mrs. Ross' patient, Ella, was functioning at Level I. Ella was generally mute, might say one or two words when spoken to; whenever she spoke spontaneously, the words seemed highly irrelevant and lacked any external referent. There was seldom any variation in the intensity of her speech; it tended to be dull and monotonous in pitch and, at the same time, unpredictable in content. Her gestures and her mannerisms seldom communicated anything, and her facial expressions did not utilize the patterns common to our culture for expressing emotions or inner experiences. She seemed on most occasions to be in a dreamlike state and did not seem to focus attention at all on people or the activities about her. She seldom knew her own name or even that she was a person. She was totally unaware of where she was or where she had been born, never knew what year or what time of day it was; she seemed to be totally unaware of the passage of time. On infrequent occasions, though she was in her fifties, she would indicate that she was seventeen or eighteen years old, and then at another time eight or nine years old. Whenever she was asked how old she was, one had the feeling in each instance that she was simply offering a guess or almost any answer to meet the expectation of the other person, as if she herself had no convictions about the validity of her response. She was extremely slovenly, paid no attention to her clothing, hair, or general appearance. Without the constant attention of personnel, she probably would not dress, would be extremely unkempt or filthy. Her musculature lacked the usual degree of tonus, her body seemed almost to be made of sponge rubber, and her musculature seemed to flow in response to the demands of gravity. She needed to be constantly looked after almost as if a child and could seldom do anything independently; whenever she did act on her own it was only with constant urging on the part of others. Whatever spontaneous activity she did engage in was generally meaningless or bizarre to others, and she was unable to explain these actions in any way. Her gait would be frequently unsteady, and one had the feeling that she had little control over her motor behavior, which was frequently aimless and expressed severe tension. Even her body temperature varied a great deal and other bodily rhythms were similarly disrupted; her sleeping was not cyclic and patterned, and this was equally true of eating and elimination. She did not interact with other patients and in general tended to be quite withdrawn, sitting by herself and seldom acknowledging the presense of others. Ella had very little capacity to differentiate among other people and was unable to call patients by name who had shared the ward with her for as much as ten years. Equally, she seemed to be unable to tell the difference between objects and people and would frequently talk to things. Because of her apathy and withdrawal, one could hardly tell whether delusions or hallucinations were present, although most of the aides had the feeling they were. In general she was characterized by a quality of blandness; one saw very little emotional reaction other than on occasions of severe and painful kinds of distress. Although there were periods when she would sit in a chair and move her limbs in masturbatory-like activities, she showed no interest in sex and seemed to have no awareness of her role as a woman. Mrs. Ross found that she could not assume that Ella knew who she was or that she knew Mrs. Ross was her aide. In both instances she had to reaffirm continually Ella's existence through almost constant intrusion into her chaotic experience. Ella could perform only the most simple of tasks and she required a great deal of body contact with Mrs. Ross in order to experience any kind of awareness.

On the other hand Mae, Mrs. Jones' patient, was generally agreed upon as functioning at Level III. Mae would frequently initiate conversations, would speak when spoken to; however, the content of her speech usually concerned physical complaints or requests for oral supplies such as food or coffee. She seldom talked about anything beyond the immediate sensory experience of her own body. She could generally describe her bodily reactions adequately; however, she could not be depended upon to give an adequate description of her emotional needs or feelings. She would usually talk in a normal tone, but occasionally, under the impact of intense feelings, her voice would become extremely shrill or would tend to drop and become very low and monotonous. She was capable of many of the facial expressions one sees in normals; but while talking with one she would frequently interrupt her natural expressions with grimacing, squinting, and a constant shifting from one foot to the other. She was usually able to attend to routine tasks, but her attention would fluctuate while attempting to follow television programs, playing cards, or during lengthy conversations. She usually knew her own name and the names of others about her, but if one were to ask her to characterize herself, describe herself as a person, or tell what she commonly felt or experienced, she could not. She seemed oriented to the ward and to the hospital most of the time but seemed to have little conception of distances or directions outside the immediately adjacent geographic area. So, too, at times she was fairly well oriented to immediate day-to-day events, but seemed unable to comprehend greater lengths of time such as a week or a month. She would seem to know she was going home for a visit within a week, but as the time drew near no one saw her preparing for the visit. It was as though the visit still was something far off in the distant future for her. In her appearance, she would dress in a generally feminine way but, nonetheless, inappropriately for the occasion; she would overdress for housekeeping or put on a housedress to go to evening activities. Her interest in her personal appearance tended to fluctuate and to be unmodulated; she might, for example, be extremely concerned about her hair, but disregard the fact that she had not taken a bath for two weeks. Mae's bodily posture was usually appropriate for the occasion, but was rather posed and deliberate, as though she were practicing a part which took conscious effort. In her performance Mae was generally capable of doing the familiar routine, feminine tasks such as scrubbing floors, washing dishes, and making beds. It was difficult for her, however, to learn to do new and unfamiliar tasks. It was hard for her to pace her work; she would work in spurts and at times would appear to be somewhat apathetic and negativistic about it; generally, she would not accomplish tasks unless there was someone about who would step in on occasion and keep her on the track. She seemed to have fair control over her gross musculature, but would sometimes have difficulty with fine muscle control so that sewing or writing was frequently difficult for her. Except during periods of stress her body rhythms were relatively well ordered. Under these circumstances one could expect some regression on Mae's part: menstruation would stop, appetite would be lost, sleeping would be disrupted. Among the patients she had a tendency to be something of a lone wolf, although it was obvious that she was extremely observant of what was going on among the others. If her curiosity was piqued, she would ask questions of them, would on occasions do things "to" or "for" other patients, but seldom would participate in anything "with" them. In her observations of others she frequently misinterpreted their activities or intentions and sometimes her temper would flare and she would become very bossy or vituperative with them and consequently was frequently rejected. Under stress it was obvious that she was overtly delusional, and in periods of low stress the aides frequently felt that the delusions were there but did not interfere with her daily activities and the carrying out of routine tasks. Ideas of reference were common with Mae but she seldom displayed any overt evidence of hallucinations; occasionally, however, the aides did infer that sudden lapses in behavior were probably due to the intrusion of hallucinations. Her expression of emotion tended to be stilted, overdone and unmodulated; a small incident might lead to an angry explosion or something mildly humorous might be reacted to with loud, prolonged laughter. Despite the unmodulated quality of her emotional reaction, however, she did tend to react emotionally to those things which affected her personally; but something happening to another patient would in all likelihood not prompt any emotional response from her. Emotional control was a problem for her and a simple and unchanging routine in the presence of an aide was necessary to maintain control; usually a few words from an aide and a short talk about what had bothered her would help her to reestablish control. Mae did display some interest in men, but seemed to be extremely uncertain of herself with them. On occasion she would become quite frightened or angry, vituperative or overly aggressive with them. She seemed to be aware of herself as a woman, but her efforts to behave as one in her relations with other women and men were clumsy and exaggerated. Here as in other areas the presence of the aide was extremely important in maintaining control.

With someone such as Mae the aides found most useful their knowledge of the patient, their ability to identify through observation of the situation what was troubling her, the maintenance of a stable, slow-moving routine, the protection of the patient from anything novel or overwhelming, and an attitude of firmness and control. The aides also discovered that there were occasions when the patient was able to talk about her feelings; when the patient did seem ready to confide, it was important for the aide to step in, try to help the patient talk about her feelings, label them, understand them. While the major emphasis was on stability and control, usually the aide found that it was also necessary to introduce new activities and experiences, but very slowly in a low-intensity, controlled fashion.

In the foregoing fashion patients were identified at each of the three remaining levels. It was possible to go through the nursing notes written by the aides about each of these patients and cull out statements the aides had made about them in their observations. It was these statements, then, that formed the pool out of which descriptions were written in the aides' language of patients at each of these five levels. In further discussions all of the patients on the ward were then categorized within the five levels. At the same time, it became obvious that the statements referred to a number of categories of behavior, such as speech, attention span, orientation, appearance, performance, motor control, bodily rhythm, social interaction, delusions, hallucinations, emotional response, and sexual behavior.

In discussing treatment strategies at each of these levels large areas of consensus emerged among the aides that were consistent with the theory; viz., the aide-patient interaction, activities the patients engaged in, and the goals held in common for patients at each of these levels.

There were definite qualities that differentiated the aide-patient relationship at each of these three levels. The aides did not experience the Level I patient as capable of initiating a relationship. They felt totally responsible for bringing about a relationship by intruding their physical presence forcefully into the everyday experiences of the patient. The aide felt her task was to become a constant and stable frame of reference for the patient's physical experience of herself. She generally relied a great deal upon physical contact with the patient and emphasized the defining of bodily limits and boundaries; many of the treatment techniques used with these patients involved such things as mirror therapy, that is, calling the patient before a mirror, pinching her ear, asking her whose ear it was; the use of baths in a manner akin to hydrotherapy;

and the use of massages to make her aware that her own body was experiencing and reacting to stimulation. Any tendency toward regression into mobility or excitement was combated by having the patient perform gross muscular activities, such as folding clothing, tearing rags, pushing the mop.

A mute catatonic patient, Sue, spent much of her time sitting quietly in a chair on the dayhall. During the course of the day the aide would frequently sit holding Sue's hand and begin talking softly to her. In talking the aide might take any one of a number of directions; she might comment on the facial expression of the patient, point out that her face looked sad; or touch the patient's face, and indicate how the corners of her lips were drawn downward. The aide sometimes would comment that the patient had moved back in her chair when touched and seemed not to want to be touched. On occasions she would take the patient's hand in hers and tell her that she was perspiring, that her hand felt hot, hotter than the aide's; the aide might ask the patient to touch her hand, and then her own to see if this were not so.

At Level I the emphasis was on bodily identification and physical contact; the goal was for the patient to experience her physical boundaries as finite, and encapsulating her psychological experiences. Communications were necessarily simple, concrete, direct, and consistent. Between the patient and the aide the nonverbal aspects of communication, that is, gestures, tone of voice, bodily posture or intensity of movement took on the greatest importance. It was also crucial that these physical contacts be consistent with the verbal aspect of communication. Simplification of the external environment was a necessity; therefore all activities were concentrated on the ward and aimed towards establishing a firm relationship with the two aides who dealt directly with the patient. Contacts with other personnel were limited so that the partner aides could provide a highly consistent, simple, stable frame of reference. The patients did not participate in any adjunctive therapy activities unless these activities were conducted by the aides.

In contradistinction to Level I, with the Level III patient the aide assumed that the patient would recognize her; the goal was for the patient to come to know the aide as a person, with the major emphasis in their relationship on the quality and appropriateness of the psychological feelings existing between the two. The aide had the major responsibility for clarifying and defining what these feelings were and what experiences and interactions had engendered them. While the aide's major concern with the Level I patient was helping her learn the limits of her body, with the Level III patient the aide's main responsibility was helping the patient learn the limits of her psyche, as well as how to distiguish between her own emotions and those of others. It was evident that at this level there was an increased emphasis on verbal communications; nevertheless at this stage the patient was expected to test the aide's words and intentions, either by resistance and opposition or by imitation and experimentation. While the aide accepted and encouraged the patient's efforts at contacting and testing reality, she also channeled these behaviors into patterns more consistent with promoting identity in the patient. Especially in the area of sexual identity the aide attempted to help the patient become aware of herself as a woman with all the associated implications for dress, mannerisms, skills, and personal relationships. The patient was expected to be aware of her physiological needs and able to assume responsibility for dealing with them; however, under stress or in novel or highly complex situations she might still experience transient episodes of confused bodily feelings. The aides tried to utilize their relationship to help the patient become more aware of her reactions to persons, things, and events in her environment, and to help the patient institute control over these feelings. Because of the need for control, the aide generally maintained a firm, intrusive approach with the patient, but also tried to provide individual time with each patient for the work of talking and labeling. At this level, then, the aide-patient relationship was characterized by control, intrusion into the patient's budding psychology, and labeling, with the goal of helping the patient experience the aide as a person and, consequently, herself as a person.

At Level IV the patient was beginning to consolidate

her psychological identity and was beginning to become much more aware of herself as a member of a social group; that is, she realized much more keenly her identity in a social sense. At this level the aides were primarily concerned with trying to make the patient aware of her own skills for contribution to the micro-society of the ward and later to the larger society of the family and the community. The aides encouraged the patients to develop outside contacts and interests. Emphasis on group interaction, homemaking, or jobs was the main focus at this level. If the Level I patient was somewhat like a new infant, the Level IV patient resembled an adolescent; consequently, major emphasis here was on the patient's development of a social role as a person living, not just in conjunction with an aide, but also with a ward, hospital, family and community. This social growth necessitated the relaxation of a firm attitude on the part of the aides; while frankness and openness still characterized the relationship, the aide did not operate in as directive a fashion as on the lower levels. The patient generally was encouraged to make at least some of her own decisions. There was a tolerance for errors on the patient's part, but the emphasis was on his learning from these errors, i.e., experiencing the consequences of his behavior. The model aide-patient relationship was that of two individuals sharing responsibilities for a common task, each sensitive to the other's feelings and supportive of them. However, the aide led the way and provided the model for the relationship. Moreover, the patient was generally encouraged to develop other meaningful relationships with other patients, personnel and volunteers in the hospital, and eventually with others in the community outside the hospital. Treatment generally seemed to be aimed at giving the patient the opportunity to experiment with taking responsibility in social situations. On the ward under certain circumstances she was directly responsible for the care of other patients. She participated in the planning of some ward activities. There were efforts at reinstituting contacts with her family and reinvolving her in her family situation. She was actively encouraged to go off the ward for activities and to engage in recreational and vocational interests in the community. The patient was usually permitted to handle her own money and was held responsible for its budgeting. As part of this social orientation, treatment plans included organization of cooking classes, "charm classes," and "supervised" mixed social activities such as dances, card parties, or picnics. As an example of expected behavior of patients at this level and the quality of the aides' interventions, the following illustration is offered.

> Joyce was exceedingly aggressive sexually. It was as though she felt that to be a woman in relation to men necessarily involved open, direct, physical expression of sexuality. At this point the aide working with Joyce began to see her and think of her as a young adolescent coming into puberty. The aide spent much time talking to Joyce about men, family life, etc.; during these chats the aide revealed her own feminine attitudes, thereby providing Joyce with an opportunity to incorporate and identify with these attitudes. Further, the aide helped Joyce with social skills, taught her how to dance, role-played conversations with men, taught her about the use of make-up, hair styling, dressing, etc.

The second area of consensus among the aides centered around treatment activities with patients. There were differences in the number and types of activities that patients did at each level. The Level I patients generally could perform daily a few simple, highly routine ward chores. They participated in several simple physical exercisees; they were able to provide at least minimally for their own personal care, for example, dress themselves and possibly attempt to comb their hair. They usually were able to go daily to the hospital canteen or for supervised walks out on the grounds.

The Level III patient was permitted all of the activities of the Level I patient except that she usually performed these activities at a much higher and more complex level. In addition, she generally participated in some of the evening activities at the hospital, might have an industrial assignment in some area of the hospital, attend music, occupational therapy or grooming class; she would on occasion go downtown accompanied by an aide, another patient, or possibly a volunteer, and would participate in socialization groups on the ward, e.g., a Valentine party or a "Spring Sing."

The Level IV patient would participate in all the same kinds of activities as the Level III, but at a much higher level. In addition, she would be able to handle money and supervise the care or work of some of the Level I or Level III patients. She might have a job downtown, would go off grounds alone and unaccompanied, would participate in the planning of ward activities, attend cooking classes, and attend social activities both on and off the ward.

Common goals were the third major treatment area for which there was consensus among the aides. For the Level I patient the aides seemed to have primarily three goals: (1) that the patient become at least physically aware of the aide, (2) be able to take minimal responsibility for her own physical care, and (3) be able to perform some simple, routine ward tasks. With the Level III patient the goal was to foster the patient's awareness of the aide and her fellow patients as persons, to encourage her to perform more complicated ward tasks and take responsibility for her own physical care at a higher level, as well as care for her room and personal effects. Another goal was to help the patient reach the point where she could follow a schedule of activities, get herself to and from those activities, and finally participate in an industrial assignment. With the Level IV patient the goal was also teaching the patient to perform complex ward tasks, take full responsibility for the physical and personal care of herself and her effects, to function at a job or high level industrial assignment, and use her own initiative, at least in part, to schedule her work, social and recreational activities; to take some responsibility for other patients on the ward, and in general to manage herself in a relatively autonomous fashion in budgeting, for example, or entering into community life. Perhaps the most important goal at this level was for the patient to gain perception of not only the people about her as persons, but also of herself as an individual with a definite role, relationships, and responsibilities in her own social group.

Based upon this dialogue between aides and project staff it had been possible over the months to log systematically the aides' experiences, observations, and treatment efforts with the patients. Because of the way in which this log was organized and systematized, the aides' experiences had been brought into harmony, coherence and organization by the ego psychological treatment theory described by DesLauriers. Using the log as a guide it was possible to write a description of the levels of patient functioning in the observational terminology of the aides, to establish signposts for change, improvement, and growth from level to level, and, in effect, to outline a treatment program. This guide included the characterization of the aide-patient relationship, the activities in which patients would be involved, and the treatment goals for patients at each of these levels. However, this outline was looked upon, not as a formula for treating patients, but rather as a systematic, organized, consensual description and elaboration of the project group's experience. This was really a log of how patients had come to be seen and a catalogue of what worked with their treatment, what could be expected of them and what they expected from aides; and, finally, the way in which they could realistically relate to aides.

The development of the levels system had a variety of important and profound effects on the project. The theory suited the aides' action orientation, spontaneity, emphasis upon observable behaviors and noninferential approach to the patients. As a consequence they were free to use their own personal style and to reaffirm their trust in themselves as useful to the patients.

The translation of the theory into the levels system provided the aides with a basis for thinking about their patients in process terms. It was now possible to see that the patients were not static and that over a period of time they did change. Since they now had signposts, subtle changes were recognizable and each had its implications for future treatment. They had the means of giving themselves feedback on their progress with patients, and hence were more capable of obviating the frustration arising from their sense of hopelessness about the patient's condition. The availability of signposts cut down on the frustration due to the aimlessness of non-goal directed behavior. Earlier in the project when the aides had become extremely frustrated by the lack of progress in patients, they would try something, anything; in most cases these measures would fail and only increase the aides' frustration. In one instance a younger patient, who had emerged out of a psychotic stupor and then not moved for some time, was placed in the hospital's school for adolescents. This "promotion" was much beyond the patient's potential performance and resulted in a regression. However, once the aides had available to them signposts such as the levels system gave, this kind of aimless trial and error was no longer necessary.

Further, the levels system provided the aides with an opportunity for more realistic goal setting that gave their activities meaning and direction. If Mae were mute, apathetic, withdrawn, isolated and unable to participate in any activities at all, then it was obvious that the aide did not have to expect Mae to leave the hospital next week. Rather, to get Mae to recognize the aide and to learn her name would be a major victory. Until this progress many of the other possibilities were totally unrealistic. Consequently, this down-to-earth approach permitted the aides to trim their previous expectations and to set up realistic sub-goals that would eventually lead to the achievement of such major ones as the patient's getting a job or leaving the hospital.

In addition, the concretization of the theory had other effects with important implications for the project. First of all, the use of levels provided all of the project personnel with a consensual language which enabled them to communicate much better than before. Concomitant to this, the group's cohesion increased. The project had worked together to invent their own unique jargon. An understanding of this jargon, more sophistication and knowledge about its use became one of the signs of being a member of the project group. Further, it demonstrated the staff's respect and trust in the aides. The staff had indicated confidence in the aides' capacity to utilize their observations to establish in participation with others a series of systematic and interrelated concepts useful in charting progress and establishing goals for patients.

In the long run, however, perhaps one of the most supportive aspects for the aides of the development of the levels system was its specification of their accountability. Since all of the project group knew the system, then all were able to have more realistic expectations for patients, and consequently more realistic expectations of what the aides could accomplish with patients. For example, it was no longer possible for someone to hold the aides responsible for getting a Level I patient out of the hospital. Now a consensual agreement had been reached that the immediate goal was not getting the Level I patient out of the hospital, but was simply helping her to enter some kind of rudimentary relationship with the aide. Therefore, the aide did not have to feel accountable for the implementation of an impossible goal; she knew more clearly what she was responsible for and now had systematic answers for those who might hold her accountable in an unrealistic fashion.

For the entire project throughout its duration the central concept of the levels system provided a tool with continuing utility for innovation. For example, later on in the project the aides were able to see that the ward structure had limitations in the treatment of the Level IV patients. And it was here that the aides began to produce many ideas concerning their needs. Level IV patients needed less supervision, a living situation much more analogous to a home or apartment living; they also needed more opportunities to experiment with their life patterns and to take greater responsibility for themselves. The aides began a series of discussions with the project staff about alternative plans for implementing these new ideas. Later on the levels concept also provided the structure that enabled the project to develop a systematic in-service training program for the aides. This development will be discussed in a later chapter.

The members of the research team on the project also found the levels concept to be useful. They were able to pick up the repertoire of descriptive statements and the various categories of patient behavior described by the aides and use this material in building an instrument to evaluate patient progress. After a number of months of work the researchers on the project were able to put together what came to be called a Behavioral Inventory Scale*; this scale was made up of descriptions of patient behavior made by aides and ordered according to levels

* The Scale is presented in Appendix A.

of functioning. Aides were interviewed periodically and asked to describe each of their patients. On the basis of such interviews a systematic measurement of patient progress was made providing further feedback to the aides on what was happening with their patients. When the scale was looked at from an overall point of view, it also provided an opportunity for reevaluation of the ward program as a whole.

In summary, then, the evolvement of the levels concept had the potential to develop in the aides the competence and capacity to think in process terms about their patients so that they might more adequately generalize their experience, establish more realistic goals, and make innovations in the program in a manner harmonious with the treatment theory. In a real sense, the levels system made the aides less dependent upon the professional staff. In addition, the system established boundaries, a framework in which the project could function in a more differentiated and systematic manner; it provided further a baseline from which judgments could be made about the degree of appropriateness and relevancy of these particular aspects of the program, namely aide behavior and goals for patients.

There was a kind of analogy between the process of treatment of a schizophrenic and the process of development of the project. In treating the schizophrenic who begins as a kind of undifferentiated mass of experiences, one works to help the patient clarify, systematize, and integrate his experiences. And so it was with the project; it had begun in an undifferentiated manner and had now reached the point where at least it could conceptualize its task and its function of patient treatment in a more systematic, organized, and integrated fashion. The project had developed an anchoring concept to which the description and evaluation of patients, the treatment program, in-service training program, aide accountability, and research evaluation could all be meaningfully tied and integrated. Finally, because it had made the aides more independent, because it had enabled them to appraise their performance and set goals and, hence, use their responsibility and their role more autonomously, the levels system permitted the project directors to withdraw more easily from the ward. The aides and the consulting staff were no longer dependent upon the project directors for theoretical awareness. Ideas and a systematic organization of the previous year's experience into a conceptual schema could now be substituted for personalities.

THE HOSPITAL-PROJECT RELATIONSHIP

As has been indicated above, numerous frictions had arisen between the project members and the remainder of the hospital organization. The project directors were concerned with maintaining the integrity of the project and for this endeavor required the cooperation of the project staff; but certainly just as essential was the support and cooperation of much of the remainder of the hospital staff. Many of these people had frequent contacts with the project and frictions usually arose at this meeting point. It was evident that on Ward H a new culture, different from the culture of the remainder of the hospital in some important respects, was being generated; when the two cultures came into contact, conflict usually resulted.

It was not so much that the ideas utilized on Ward H were alien to the rest of the hospital; many of the ideas for this project existed in some fashion elsewhere in the hospital. But while before they had been incorporated into the usual on-going structure, on the project they had been systematically related and a new structure evolved to contain them. Whereas in the general hospital culture the lines of decision making, role definitions, and authority relationships operating among personnel were clear, on H this was not always the case; and even when clear, these boundaries of authority were different from the rest of the hospital. Generally on H there were few hard and fast rules about decision making; rather, the likelihood was that any decision needed to be negotiated. There were few prescriptions to define the interrelationships existing among the project personnel. Many of the usual procedures employed in the rest of the hospital were not followed on Ward H.

The business office was perhaps most frequently made aware of the way in which Ward H did not follow usual procedures. First the aides decided to keep the patients' money in lockers on the ward rather than in the business office, as was the usual practice. Then the aides would take the initiative in telling some patients who had gotten jobs that they should start paying their hospital bill. Whenever the service departments of the hospital, such as maintenance, dietary or the laundry, objected to unorthodox procedures on Ward H, the complaints would have to be handled by the business office. Patient problems which the business office would normally discuss with the ward doctor, section chief, or nurse, now had to be directed to the aide in charge of that particular patient.

The disagreement with the dietary department arose in the early days of the project. Initially the Ward H patients ate in a dining room on Ward E. Every day the women marched over to that ward, rushed through their meal, and marched back. The aides thought that life would be much simpler if their patients could stay on Ward H to eat. There wouldn't be the confusion of moving from one ward to the other for every meal, and mealtime could become part of the therapeutic milieu.

The dietary department was opposed to this change for a number of reasons: there were the problems of dirty dishes, health regulations, and the necessity to keep the area clean. In response to each of these objections the Ward H aides asked to be given the material, e.g., sink, garbage disposer, stove, so their ward could qualify as a dining room. Given the equipment, they said, they would do the work themselves. The dietary department finally agreed to bring food carts up from the kitchen onto the ward and leave the rest of the mealtime arrangements to the people on the ward. This procedure seems to have proved successful, but it was difficult to say whether some bad feelings still existed as a result of this change.

There was a misunderstanding with the chaplains. The aides had found that distinguishing between daytime and nighttime was difficult for these patients. For some it was a nightmare. In order to make the situation easier by establishing a formal ritual to mark the boundary between day and night activities, the afternoon aides decided to conduct vesper services. This practice had been going on for some time before the project directors learned that the chaplains felt the aides should have involved them in planning this

activity. By the time the difficulty was discovered, most of
the high feelings had subsided, but the whole incident led
a project member to conclude: "You rarely find out you are
threatening someone until it has become a dead issue and
the position irretrievable."

In an effort to obtain some perspective the project directors called in outside consultants. Two social psychologists whose field of specialty was that of organizational
analysis were asked to evaluate the project. Their focus
was somewhat different from that of Dr. Key: whereas
Dr. Key focused upon the organizational difficulties inherent within the project and only tangentially with the
way in which they created problems in the project's relationship to the hospital, these consultants focused directly upon the hospital and the problems created for it
by the presence of the project.

First of all, they pointed out that the hospital as a
whole was a large social organization made up of interdependent members. If the members of this organization
were to function in a cohesive, viable way, certain norms
or rules governing procedures, behaviors, expectations,
and roles had to prevail. Some of these rules were explicit;
most, of course, were implicit. The project staff, however,
while still members of the larger hospital organization,
had evolved a different set of norms for their own structure. Whenever these two bodies came into contact, then,
the norms clashed and practices that held in one part of
the organization did not hold in another. This inconsistency, of course, tended to provoke discomfort, anxiety,
and a sense of threat. Perhaps nowhere were the norms
more different than those governing the relationship between aides and professional staff. In general for the rest
of the hospital the professional staff regarded themselves
as the individuals who treated the patients; it was the
aides who were there merely to help. On H it was the
aides who treated the patients and the professional staff
was there to help.

It has been indicated earlier that the hospital used a
supervisory system common to the administrative structure of mental hospitals. Most members of the organiza-

tion had dual loyalties and were supervised by two individuals. In one instance they had a loyalty to their own disciplinary group and received supervision from the head of their department or his surrogate. On the other hand they were also loyal to the particular functional unit where they were assigned and received supervision and direction from the head of that unit. For those members of the project staff this divided loyalty created an immense difficulty because of the normative differences discussed above. Most of the project staff received supervision both from the project directors, who enforced one set of norms, and also from the department heads who enforced another. This dual supervision created a great deal of anxiety and conflict over loyalties. This conflict, at least up to now, had not been openly recognized; yet in the case of the ward nurse the conflict had reached such proportions that she found the situation intolerable and found it necessary to leave the project.

These two consultants pointed out that many of the project's difficulties stemmed from a lack of appreciation of group structure and functioning. They stated that the major violation of group functioning had been changing the roles of the people involved in the project without adequately preparing the remainder of the hospital group. They also indicated that an individual cannot violate or deviate from the norms of his group unless the conflicts that such deviation arouses are resolved and he has the permission of his peer group, a step not taken with any of the project personnel. In a certain sense, then, each member of the project staff had been considered a traitor by his own discipline. Also, the project staff was functioning in a way inconsistent with the way in which the remainder of the group defined their roles. All of the disciplines felt threatened at one time or another by the changes made in Ward H. Sometimes the threat came from a specific incident; in other cases, the underlying premises of the project seemed a challenge to the professional image of various disciplines. Many of the disciplines believed that the manner in which their group members functioned in the project was demeaning to the "professional image" of that discipline; consequently many of the project staff found themselves caught between the devil and the deep blue sea with very little support from either the devil or the deep blue sea.

The two consultants had observed that the placement of first-year residents on the ward had been an effort to mitigate some of this conflict and to reduce the normative differences between H and the rest of the hospital. However, while the presence of the first-year resident on Ward H was consistent with the procedure of the rest of the hospital, the kind of role asked of him was not; it was a deviation which could only increase the strain on the hospital and project members.

Many points of conflict between the project and the hospital have been pointed out. Generally conflicts arose out of differences in procedures and role definitions. The consultants pointed to the differences in norms that were basic to these conflicts. They were able to point out that the members of the project belonged to both normative groups and had not received the support of either for deviating from the norms of the other.

In an attempt to cope with the situation described by the consultants, the project directors arranged for most of the upper echelon administrative personnel (the department heads in the hospital and the administrative personnel on the hospital section where the project ward was located) to have a day-long meeting away from the hospital. This was to be an unstructured meeting where many of the feelings about the project not worked out in the past could now be brought into the open and hopefully resolved. While the meeting did not live up to the promise of resolution, it did enable both the project directors and much of the hospital staff to communicate more clearly their perceptions of one another, to understand the kinds of difficulties that each was working with, and to clarify many of the issues at stake. As these channels of communication were opened up, as the concerns of many of the hospital staff were voiced, and as the project directors were able to provide information about the project to the hospital staff, many of the issues underlying the hospital-project relationship emerged as exceedingly complex and unamenable to any simple solutions. However, an awareness of each other's concerns, the exchange of perceptions, had an ameliorative effect. Issues, points of difference, and conflict could now be looked at more openly, more tolerantly, and frequently dealt with more constructively.

SUMMARY

In retrospect, this year had been one of analysis. The problems experienced near the end of the previous year had been studied intensively. Solutions were sought for the problems that lay solely within the limits of the project, that is, providing the aides with the means for thinking of their patients in process terms and enabling them to set goals for their patients. The core concept of levels had been evolved. The other problems that involved the hospital and the supporting staff were studied and, by the spring of 1962, based upon the earlier period of study, there was much active planning within the project and within the hospital to solve these problems. Many alternatives were considered, and eventually a variety of solutions compatible with both the needs of the hospital and the aims of the project was devised and ready to be put into effect in July 1962.

Obviously the project would now have to reorient itself and focus upon the problems of the supporting staff. The evaluations of the consultants and the experience of the project staff had all underscored the need for role clarification among the supporting staff. It was clear that these individuals functioned on the borderline between the two organizations, the project and the hospital. Neither organization could change its expectations of the supporting staff; yet this dual set of expectations, especially when unclear, vague, and without the means for achieving either alternative, had created an intolerable degree of anxiety in the supporting staff and interfered with the development of their capacity to support the aides. Hopefully, clarification of the staff's role and the development of a system for their support and training would enable them to function more adequately in both systems. Because the project staff's difficulty in supporting the aides caused a loss of momentum among the aides and a drop in the frequency of aide-patient contacts, a resolution was essential to the project's growth.

6

The Structure and Evolvement of the Support System—The Third Year

Many problems had arisen by the end of the first year, and with the help of consultants these had been subjected to study and analysis during the second year. Many solutions were proposed and some chosen for application at the beginning of the third year. The first of these solutions was to transfer the administrative responsibility for Ward H from the clinical department of the hospital to the research department. Ward H was no longer considered a clinical and training area but rather a research area. Much of the conflict during the first years had arisen between the ward and the hospital. Each had different norms, roles, and administrative practices. Transfer of Ward H to the research department of the hospital seemed to be the most expedient way of reducing this conflict. Since the ward was no longer a training area, first year residents were not assigned there. However, an agreement was made that the ward could be used as an area for the training of advanced residents. It was assumed that advanced residents could function within the role of consultant and find this training valuable without encountering many of the problems of the first-year resident. This decision was to be optional for the resident, but the project directors were to remain free to select this individual. Generally these people were assigned to another section of the hospital, but then would devote approximately eight hours per week to the project as a part-time assignment. Because of the administrative transfer of the ward, the project directors had more control over the selection of the ward staff. By this means they were able to maintain more adequately the integrity of the project and to reduce much of the conflict between the project and the hospital.

Another change put into effect at this time was the

withdrawal of one of the project directors from the ward. The consultants had pointed to the difficulties caused by his functioning in multiple roles, which did not provide maximum opportunity for role development on the part of others. His withdrawal created an opportunity for the growth of other individuals. His multiple roles were separated and each became available to separate persons for development. Since the nurse was no longer to be considered a research member of the project, her multiple role was also eliminated. Her responsibilities were limited to the ward and the aides. In addition, an in-service training program was to be established and other members of the hospital staff were to function in the role of educators.

These changes had the additional impact of furthering the clarification of levels of responsibility. The aides were fully responsible for the patients. The ward staff, that is, the nurse, the social worker, and the psychiatric resident were fully responsible for the functioning of the aides. However, this group did have the help of the educational staff who were responsible for the training of the aides. The project directors were responsible for the project as a whole, including program development and evaluation.

When these changes were put into effect, the project concentrated its energies on development of the ward professional staff. As indicated above, the function of this group was to provide support for the aides. In the development of this support system four factors appeared important: first, it was necessary to provide an opportunity for the role definition and development of each member of the ward professional staff; second, it would also be important to provide a supportive supervisory system for them in their efforts at role development; third, it was necessary to arrive by consensus at a cognitive structure or a theoretical schema to outline guiding principles for the ward professional staff in the practice of their roles. As the levels system had been devised by the project for the work of the aides, the notion of consulting supervision was developed as a guide for the work of the supporting personnel. Fourth and finally, there was an obvious need for the further development of administrative structure and practices consistent with the original principles of the project. In separating itself from the clinical area of the hospital, the project no longer needed to rely upon the standard administrative practices; thus it was now free to evolve its own administrative principles.

ROLE DEFINITION

Since many of the professional staff (the nurse, psychiatric resident, and educators) were new to the project there was a salient need to clarify their responsibilities for them and to provide a forum for discussion of these expectations, as well as an opportunity for an orientation to the goals of the project. Consequently, early in the summer of the third year the project staff gathered away from the hospital for a full day's workshop; this workshop focused primarily upon the project directors' expectations of the staff and a definition of their responsibilities. In the discussions that followed, the efforts of the group were directed toward gleaning the best ideas from the past experience of the project with these roles; from this historical perspective were defined tentative roles for the various project professional personnel. Hopefully they would return to the project and experimentally test themselves in these roles in an effort to understand the issues for themselves. The workshop ended with an agreement to try these new roles and to discuss their experiences with them at a second workshop to be held two months later.

During the second workshop the project group reviewed the members' experiences with their various roles. Many inconsistencies had been spotlighted and many problems clarified. For example, the social worker seriously questioned whether it was possible for the aides to work with families or whether both she and the aides should share work with families. The nurse indicated that her primary problem was knowing an alternative when she did not agree with the aide's particular approach to a patient. When she felt it necessary to intervene in such a situation, she had difficulty understanding how she might in a manner consistent with the principles of the project and still provide the leadership that was expected of her.

Her concern about leadership was shared by the aides, one of whom expressed it as follows:

I think I voice the concern of every aide here when I say the patients have the aides that they can go to for support. Right now the aides have really no one to go to. I live over by the railroad tracks and the other evening I was standing by the sink washing dishes and the train was switching on the tracks and immediately the thought came to me that we are a bunch of boxcars all loaded with cargo. We have everything that it takes to run with. I am sitting on one track over here, another boxcar loaded sitting over here on this track. Well, the first thing you are going to have to do is to get all these boxcars on the same track. Okay, we get them all on the same track and get them connected. Well, we are all just on the same track, connected, ready to go, but still we don't move. Well, the next thing we are going to have to do is to get a powerful diesel engine and put it in front of these boxcars. Okay, we get a diesel engine and connect it to the boxcars that are loaded to go. Well, we are still right there and we aren't going anywhere. Well, then, common sense would tell anybody that we are going to have to give it an engineer to put in that engine and with some specific instructions of where to go and where we unload this cargo. Well, there is nothing to keep the boxcars from traveling on then; we have everything that it takes.

At another point in the workshop the same aide commented upon the lack of clarity concerning roles among the supporting staff and its effect upon the aides.

You know when I heard Miss B (Supervising Nurse) just now; she said one statement that really struck me. She said "not made clear." There have been so many things that really haven't been made clear from the very beginning and that is the reason we are in such a turmoil. I was wondering when it was started whether it was really clearly planned. No one stopped to think that all of these things would come up. We were all very enthusiastic. We all grabbed hands. There was a pond in front of us and we all just jumped in the pond. Well, okay, here we are in the pond; we are about to sink now. So Dr. C (Project Director), he had a little more power than the rest of us; he, by some hook or crook, swam to the shore, but we are still in the pond. Well, he sympathizes with us now. He is sitting on the bank. He knows that we are sinking so, consequently, he throws in a music therapist, figuring this will help us. Well, instead of her helping us, she is sinking too. So then he throws in an occupational therapist. She is going to be another lifesaver. Well, that is just one more to add to the bunch that is sinking. Then up comes a group therapist; he throws him in. Well, instead of us getting out, it is just more of us getting in. And I really think this is what is happening. We are becoming more and more involved and the problems are getting greater and greater. No one knows what to do with it so, consequently, everybody is getting upset and is blaming everybody else, and I just don't think that the thing is working out the way we really want it to work out.

The growing number of supporting personnel on the project also had its effect on the aides' spontaneity. This was described by the psychiatric consultant during the workshop.

One big problem seems to be this, that there are many things scheduled on the ward during the course of the day. The aides are bound to some sort of schedule all the time— Mrs. C (Music Therapist) is coming, Mrs. L (Occupational Therapist) is coming, somebody else is coming, I'm coming, Dr. L (Educator) is coming—there is always somebody coming on the ward. They find it hard to be spontaneous with the patients because they are very much bound to these people coming to the ward. As Mrs. Watts said, in the old days if she suddenly got an idea that she wanted to pack up the patients and go out to Lake Shawnee she would just do it any time at all, when she suddenly got this feeling. But this is impossible now. There is always somebody coming, you always have to consider that somebody is going to be there, and this is very inhibiting.

SUPERVISORY SYSTEM

It became obvious that the occasional role definitions and discussions in the workshops were not enough; if the ward professional staff were to develop their roles, they too would need a support system wherein they could experiment, receive feedback, and develop a frame of reference for the practice of their roles.

In order to create this system, the project directors began to meet weekly with the supervisors of the ward professional personnel who included the supervisor of the ward resident, nurse, social worker, and educators. Each of the ward personnel had been meeting weekly on a one-to-one basis with his supervisor. At this point the project directors asked each of these supervisors to meet together with them to discuss the problems of their supervisees. The responsibility of this group then was the support and development of the ward professional staff. In their weekly meetings this group considered the supervisory practices each was using and discussed how consistent these practices were with the goals of the project. Out of these discussions grew several principles for supervisory practices and their effect upon role development. From this discussion was abstracted the concept of consulting supervision, generally applicable throughout the project.

CONSULTING SUPERVISION

As with other aspects of the project, the supervisory philosophy was an outgrowth of the project's overall aims, evolving naturally and consistently with the other principles of the project.

As elaborated above, central to the treatment program was the personality and the humanity of the aide; it was essential that the major elements in any supervisory process be dictated by this human core. There were four aspects of the aide's personality especially relevant to the techniques of supervision which eventually emerged. The first of these characteristics of good treatment imposed as a necessary condition for patient improvement the freedom the aide had to use herself spontaneously.

The second aspect of a successful treatment program was the belief in the importance of the individual personal style of the aide for achieving the goal of patient progress. This personal style went beyond spontaneity in and of itself and referred to the more enduring aspects of the aide's personality, including her beliefs, attitudes and aptitudes, and the unique way in which she expressed them.

Third was the respect for the aides as action-oriented and goal-directed people. Their approach to tasks was to set goals for themselves and then do, in ways that were consistent with their style, whatever was necessary to reach these goals. The staff encouraged this dynamic approach.

Finally, the treatment program was based on the belief in the aide's adaptability to new circumstances as they arose, i.e., the capacity to redirect their efforts when realistic circumstances made it appropriate for them to do so.

These elements of the treatment program provided certain dimensions for the supervisory procedure that developed. Such a procedure should not inhibit spontaneity, but should encourage personal style so that the solution of problems was left to whatever techniques best fit the personality of the particular supervisee. This had to be done with full knowledge that personal style would differ from one supervisee to the next; also the way the supervisor would cope with the problem would probably differ from the supervisee's way. It also demanded that the procedure should provide the impetus for change when needed.

The need for support was one other crucial element that transcended the core aspects of the treatment program mentioned above. To be consistent with the attitude the project had toward the aides, this support had to provide for learning from mistakes and to assume that the supervisee's attitude toward his mistakes was a responsible one. Finally, the supervisor had to demonstrate involvement with the supervisee's experiences.

With the outline of these various essential dimensions of a supervisory procedure completed, all that was now required was the elucidation and the codification of this philosophy. The resulting procedure became known as consulting supervision.

As implied above, the basic assumption in consulting supervision was that there was no single best way for persons to relate to each other, whether they be patients or professionals dealing with patients.

The basic tenets of consulting supervision were the following:

(1) The supervisee determines the goal he wants to attain

(2) The supervisee may use any procedure to attain his goal

(3) While the supervisee is not accountable to a supervisor for the procedures he uses, he is accountable to the supervisor for their results and the extent to which these results conform to the goals he has set

(4) The supervisor is free to criticize and, in fact, should mention any observations, information, reservations, disagreements, alternatives, or new ideas that he has to the supervisee

(5) The supervisee must responsibly consider such ideas from the supervisor

(6) The supervisee is free to accept or reject any of these ideas

(7) The supervisor should temper or avoid any recommendations if he senses that the supervisee is reacting to such ideas as orders

(8) The supervisor is oriented toward helping the supervisee become aware of patterns in his personal style

(9) The supervisee is responsible for the consequences of his personal style.

These tenets form the basis for the process of consulting supervision systematically introduced throughout the project. The project directors believed that the procedure was essential, not only to the progress of the patients on the ward, but also to the growth and development of all project personnel who were experimenting with new ways of functioning. Since consulting supervision was based upon the idea that people react to others the way they are reacted to, this procedure could not be introduced at only one supervisory level. Rather, the procedure would have to permeate all levels of supervision and consequently there would be a parallel process set in motion. All supervisors would serve as models for those who were responsible to them.

The question may be asked what are the safeguards and controls against human failure and error that might occur with this form of supervision? There are three major safeguards that are inherent in this process. First, the supervisee is held accountable, both for the achievement of his goals and the consequences of his chosen courses of action.

Second, the supervisor is obliged to discuss with the

supervisee any reservations he may have. The supervisee in turn is obliged to consider these reservations with his supervisor. While he is free to reject these reservations he remains responsible and accountable for the consequences of his choice.

The third safeguard derives from the use of personal style basic to consulting supervision. Inherent in healthy personalities is a self-consistency which manifests itself in day to day behavior. The more free the individual is to use his personality, the more evident are these internal consistencies. The interaction of these internally consistent factors with the external situation provides for the consultant supervisor an understandable process that is itself both consistent and predictable. Theories of change assume that the presence of such a process makes it possible to influence the participants in that process. Since the consultant supervisor has a consistent process to follow, it is amenable to influence.

It might be helpful to differentiate consulting supervision from other more traditional supervisory practices. For this purpose three such traditional forms have been chosen. These will be compared with consulting supervision on several variables. Rather than restate the ideas involved in consulting supervision, the following will deal only with the most evident differences. For each of the following statements then the assumption is that the consulting supervision process that has been outlined differs from this process. It is appreciated that there are areas of commonality.

In direct supervision the supervisor determines both method and goal with the supervisee being held accountable for both. The supervisor is assumed to be more competent and to know best. The supervisor sets the goal which does not usually include the personal growth of the supervisee. The demand made of the supervisee is essentially one of compliance.

The traditional form of psychotherapy supervision is essentially a training process but one in which the emphasis is upon method more than upon results. The implicit demand in the traditional situation is that the supervisee identify with the *method* of the supervisor.

The supervisee is competent to the extent that he is able to use the supervisor's method.

The non-directive method has been used both for the training of psychotherapy and in other forms of supervision. The climate in this procedure is one of openness but of a one-way openness, that of the supervisee toward the supervisor and it is not generally reciprocated. The demand made on the supervisee in this procedure is limited to his involvement and experiencing of the situation. Self-experience is the major goal. There is no contract for accountability.

Again it should be stated that the descriptions above are more pure forms of these other procedures and as pure forms probably exist more in theory than in actual practice; however, they still are obviously quite different from consulting supervision, both in terms of the basic assumptions made and the technical procedures involved.

ADMINISTRATIVE PRACTICES

In the two preceding sections on the supervisory system and consulting supervision an attempt was made to describe the development of administrative practices consistent with the treatment principles of the project. By the end of the third year it was apparent that administration had become a useful tool in providing the support necessary for the achievement of the project's goals. Apparent also were many similarities in the goals and the attitudes inherent in both the treatment and administrative practices of the project.

The therapist and the supervisor were both *responsible for growth* in the individuals under them; the task of both was to foster the growth of social responsibility by means of the relationship with the therapist or supervisor. Both relationships were characterized by *respect*; for the therapist and the supervisor the essential ingredient of this respect was trust in the patient's or supervisee's capacity to grow and to meet reasonable expectations. Further in both relationships the therapist or supervisor acted as a *catalytic agent*; it was his function in some way to "jog the other individual out of his rut." The therapist was oriented toward intruding into the consciousness of the patient and holding his attention to the therapist's physical presence. The supervisor, on the other hand, was free to demand the supervisee's attention and consideration of relevant issues; this particular characteristic the aides came to call "facing reality."

The therapist and the supervisor also provided identification figures for those with whom they worked; in both instances they provided a *model* of a competent adult to aid them in coping with their problems. Thus, in both sets of relationships all the supervisor or therapists really had to offer to another individual was themselves; if this self were competent, adequate, and respectful a model would be provided with which another could identify. Further, in each set of relationships the supervisor and the therapist held the other individuals *accountable for results*. Even in the therapeutic relationship, the aides expected achievement from the patient.

Both the therapists and the supervisor were concerned with the *development of identity* in the individual with whom they worked. In supervision this concern centered on the personal style of the supervisee. The supervisee was free to use his own personal style and was encouraged to test its effectiveness. In this sense the supervisee came to understand himself more fully, to expand his competencies, and to gain a greater awareness of his impact on others. Within the therapy situation the aides' major concern was with the patient's experience of herself and with the fostering of the patient's identity. Because the patients functioned at many different levels of intactness, the experience of each was different at every level. The way in which the aide demonstrated her concern with the patient's identity was similarly different. However, throughout all of the levels the development of identity remained the aides' primary concern. Finally, the supervisory and therapeutic relationships were similar in that the supervisor and the therapists were *committed* to the individuals with whom they worked; by virtue of their trust, their respect, and their concern for the other person they manifested a sense of commitment which encouraged the feeling of interpersonal security necessary to growth.

Perhaps the question could be asked, "Why was this consistency between treatment and administrative practices necessary?"[1] It was evident that if these practices were not consistent the brunt of the inconsistency would be borne by the aides who, on the one hand, were the recipients of administrative practice, and, on the other, the project's therapists. For them inconsistency could detract seriously from their effectiveness; the power of the situation to induce their growth would be considerably reduced because their administrative supervisors would be providing models inconsistent with what was being asked of them vis-à-vis the patient. Certainly the disorganizing and disruptive effect of inconsistent behavior is well established.[2] In view of its potential for the production of mental illness, the reduction of inconsistency is an important goal for the mental hospital.

In the days prior to treatment innovations when mental hospitals were considered strictly as custodial institutions designed to protect society from its inmates, one found administrative practices that were extremely consistent with attitudes toward inmates. The goal of this consistent approach was the production of a stable system: the mental patient was seen as unable to change; if anything, the course of his illness would lead to deterioration. He was in a fixed rigid class. Fixed in behavior too, was the staff of these institutions; discipline was categorized as to function, each performed a fixed duty, and the functions of each were soon relegated to an unchanging routine. Stability was demanded by the outside community. It was the function of all the hierarchical levels of the hospital to impose and to maintain stability on those levels below it. Due to this goal, a fixed, stratified, unchanging, but highly consistent society evolved in the mental institution. In contrast, consistent structures can have goals other than stability, and in the structure described above the primary goal was the promotion of

[1] For a more thorough discussion of this question see: Colorelli, N. J. and Siegel, S. M., "Administrative Structure and Treatment Goals: Dysrhythmia?" *Mental Hospitals*, Vol. 14, No. 11, pp. 608-612.

[2] Bateson, G., Jackson, D. D., Haley, J. and Weakland, J., "Toward a Theory of Schizophrenia," *Behavioral Science*, Vol. 1, 1956, pp. 251-264.

growth in the members of the system. However, the growth process in itself is not stable; therefore the system is not stable because it must be constantly adapting to the growing competency of its members. As each of the members evolves and develops his potential, so too must the system continue to evolve and pace itself to the collective growth process.

Initially the project had proposed a treatment program oriented to inducing growth in patients. However, to exploit fully the potential of this system, it became necessary to build an administrative structure that was consistent with it. The effort to use the administrative system pertinent to the rest of the hospital during the early years of the project had led to inconsistencies that precluded the attainment of the treatment goals. Out of the treatment principles of the project and the needs of the aides slowly grew an administrative structure consistent with those goals and needs.

SUMMARY

By the end of the second year the aides had clarified their responsibilities for themselves, they had developed their roles, and had participated in devising a cognitive structure for the practice of their roles. Despite this progress, however, they were unable to get satisfactory support from the ward supervisory staff for functioning within these roles. This failure had led to lowered morale and efficiency.

During the third year the project focused on this problem of support; its major task was that of the development of roles and supervisory competence among the ward supervisory staff. Responsibilities were clarified for the staff, opportunity for role development provided, a theory of role practice devised, and a support system developed via the network of supervisory meetings. These four elements were now available for both the aides and the ward supervisors. As these changes were put into effect during the third year, and more especially as the supporting staff came to appreciate its role and gain competence in its exercise, the situation of the aides improved: morale improved, aide-patient contacts increased, the discharge rate rose, and the aides initiated innovations in the program and once again began to extend themselves beyond the confines of the ward. Partially in response to the aides, but also because of increasing satisfaction in their roles, similar improvements in morale and efficiency were observed in the supervisory staff.

7

All Systems Go—The Support System—The Fourth Year

The third year had been devoted to building the support system for the professional staff. As indicated above, the achievement of this task was reflected in increased morale and effectiveness among the aides. By the beginning of the fourth year the project had become a self-sustaining system; role definitions for members of the project had been completed and each had had an opportunity to gain experience and to develop his respective role. Responsibilities had been clarified. A set of cognitive principles had been devised for therapeutic roles (the levels system) and for the supervisory roles (consulting supervision). Provision had been made for in-service training of the members of the system. A communication system had been set up; meetings were arranged, experimented with and worked out at various levels to facilitate communication throughout the project. Inherent within this communication network were methods for providing feedback on the influence of treatment and supervisory efforts. Consensus on the nature of relevant feedback had been established among the group. Finally, the norm of innovation and continued evolvement was established and facilitated by means of a monthly meeting for all the project which encouraged full interchange of ideas among all personnel, the exploration of project problems, and the consideration of novel solutions.

During the three years the original principles had been applied generally throughout the treatment, training and administrative functions of the project. From all indications at the beginning of the fourth year the system was working well. Despite a high level of activity on the ward, involvement with the patients, their families and communities, there was a notable absence of crisis. The system was able to provide for most contingencies. Despite its complexity, the system was not cumbersome and had a natural, informal flow. Because it was consistent, its complexities were not difficult to deal with. The system was geared to promote growth, not stability; there was reliance upon negotiation, rather than upon rules and precedents. And, above all, there was an increase in the discharge rate.

It is now possible to describe the Ward H project in its final year. The remainder of this chapter will be devoted to a description of the support system. The roles of the ward professional staff, those who supported them, and the in-service training program will be elaborated. In Chapter 8 the ward treatment program focusing upon the aide-patient relationship and the rationales guiding this relationship will be described.

As indicated above, the strenuous work, the intensity of interactions, and the emotional pressures made support mandatory for the aides. The provision of this support was primarily the responsibility of the ward nurse, the resident psychiatrist, and the social worker. Readily available to them was a group of educators who would perform the highly specific function of in-service training.

THE NURSE

Among all these individuals perhaps there was no one whose role was more central or more influential with the aides than the nurse. Hers was perhaps the most difficult role to develop and integrate with the project, and at the same time one of the most crucial. By the fourth year the nurse's role contained two major elements: first, she was responsible for the aides, and, second, for coordination and communication. As far as her responsibility for the aides was concerned, the nurse came to see herself as responsible for the growth of the aides as people rather than for the performance of certain organizational services. Her concern was not the patients, but rather seeing to it that the aides established treatment goals, arrived at mutual decisions consistent with those goals, considered all relevant information when making decisions, and abided by their decisions as long as they felt them to be appropriate. At the point when the aides realized that a course of action following a decision was no longer appropriate or called for a change, the nurse's concern was to see that the aide established new goals. When they had established these new goals for themselves, she held them accountable for their attainment. If a goal was not realized, she held them accountable for considering the lack of results and the use of this experience to reconsider goals.

The nurse was further responsible for evaluating the aides' performance in achieving results with the treatment of patients. Her recommendations concerning merit raises, dismissal, and probationary status were based upon the capacity of the aide to conduct responsible treatment. Above all, the nurse's most important responsibility toward the aides was providing emotional support; this support was given primarily by management of conflict among the aides, counseling, providing commentary on their behavior, giving encouragement, and having reasonable expectations of them. Hopefully, she tried to provide for the aides a climate in which they could learn the best use of themselves and through her attitude foster their training and development.

A second major aspect of her work, her function of coordination and communication, approached the traditional role of the hospital nurse except that it was more complex. Among the aides on a given shift her function was to arrange for the scheduling of activities, vacations, relief, and off-time days. It was her responsibility also to pass on information to the aides and the ward staff about new hospital policies and procedures. Again she had the duty to see that the necessary supply of medications was available. Although the ward had been physically divided into four autonomous treatment areas, the nurse had to schedule and coordinate those activities which affected the ward as a whole, such as housekeeping, linen supply, and maintenance. It was her responsibility also to keep communications open and clear between the ward professional staff and the aides. As the involvement of the ward social worker in the treatment program increased, the nurse played a key role in facilitating and passing on communications between the aides and the social worker. The nurse also had to function as a coordinator be-

tween the morning and afternoon shifts. In order to further this coordination her working hours were changed
early in the project. She worked an 8:00 A.M. to 5:00 P.M.
shift much the same as the rest of the professional staff.
This change permitted her to have two hours with the
afternoon personnel who usually came in at 3:00 P.M.
She was present at all the partner meetings. She was responsible for conducting a weekly team meeting where
all members of the ward staff were present. She was also
responsible for the scheduling of any activities that might
involve both shifts. In the final year of the project the
resident physician, the ward social worker and the nurse
began to meet weekly with a section staff psychiatrist to
coordinate their supportive efforts toward the aide staff.

Her responsibilities for communication and coordination were not restricted to the ward; anyone from outside
who had contact with the ward channeled his communications through her. She was in effect the traffic manager
for all administrative matters concerning the ward.
It was she who dealt with the dietary and maintenance
departments, and the business office. However, all patient
problems were channeled directly to the aide involved,
but the nurse was usually aware of such communications.

It was she too who maintained much of the communication with the community at large. In the last year of
the project a monthly meeting was scheduled for all project members, both those on and off the ward; in this
meeting the nurse's communications, her perspective,
were crucial.

By the final year of the project she was able to cut
down her time on the ward to four hours per day. Usually she would come in around 12:30 P.M. and would
leave the ward at 4:30 P.M. This schedule gave her some
time to be with both shifts. Her morning hours were now
free and she was able to assume responsibility for an additional ward. During this time she began to hold individual counseling sessions with the aides. She no longer
needed to observe the aides in their work; she had been
able to divest herself of her "watchdog" function. Rather,
she was able now to concentrate on helping the aides
with their problems and this help could be offered in a
supervisory session.

This final role of the nurse, however, was the result of slow development. Initially her role was very different; the changes that did occur reflected the evolution of the Ward H system and of the roles that developed in harmony with the principles of the project.

Initially, as indicated above, her role was quite vague, over-inclusive and diffuse; it contained many of the traditional elements of the nurse's role at the hospital. Only after a long period of time was the nurse able to divest herself of these. Initially the change in her traditional role was that she no longer had contact with patients. As a consequence then, early in the project the nurse's role was defined primarily in a negative way.

With the withdrawal of the project directors from the ward there was now opportunity for the development of the nurse's role. But, it was difficult for her to conceive of her function as something other than controlling aides and treating patients. She now had to be fully responsible for the aides in a new way and not concern herself with treatment of patients.

In growing into this role she had to answer questions and resolve dilemmas for herself. There were at least three major problems for her:

1. "What do you do when an aide does something with the patient that you don't think is therapeutic?" This situation frequently arose on the ward when the aide would engage in an interaction with a patient which the nurse honestly did not feel to be therapeutic; she might, in fact, see some interactions as quite harmful to the patient. How to cope with this kind of situation was one of the major problems she needed to solve. Her immediate reaction was consistent with the traditional role of the nurse; she would tell the aide that her behavior was not appropriate and ask her to stop it. This direct interference, of course, was quite inconsistent with the principles of the project. Usually this action would be followed by a swing to a *laissez-faire*, "do-nothing" attitude where she would feel that, at best, all she could do was to stand helplessly and hope that everything would come out all right. Neither of these approaches was consistent with the project and neither was supportive to the aides. Eventually the nurse was able under these circumstances

to approach the aide to remind her of the goals established previously for the patient; as a consequence, she was able to ask the aide questions about the appropriateness of the particular interaction in the light of the goals the aide herself had set up for the patient. She could insist that the aide consider the issues that troubled her. She could make sure that the aide was aware of the consequences of her behavior and her accountability. As long as the aide was aware of these elements of the situation, the course of action was up to her. In this way the nurse was able to take a much more supportive stance with the aides and, at the same time, leave their freedom, authority, and full responsibility for the patients unimpaired.

2. "What do you do when aide partners are in conflict?" Often in the course of the project the aides would disagree on the goals that needed to be set up for the patients or upon the appropriate techniques for achieving their goals. These disagreements could bring the aides into conflict which occasionally lasted for some time. Such an unresolved conflict had a highly deleterious effect, not only on the effectiveness of the aides, but on the treatment of the patients and the morale of the ward as well. The nurse was held responsible for managing these conflicts; here too she tended initially to vacillate between controlling them in an authoritarian fashion or standing back helplessly. Whenever she felt unable to cope with a problem she usually attempted to involve the psychiatric resident in its management. Over the course of the project, however, she was able to learn several techniques of conflict management that she was able to apply by herself. The first step, of course, and one that was usually sufficient, was to recognize clearly that the disagreement or conflict was real and to concentrate upon it. If her first efforts were unsuccessful and she was sure the aides would not take her advice as an order, she could offer direct suggestions or opinions, with the understanding that the aides were free to accept or reject them. She would concentrate on the consequences of the alternative decisions under consideration by the aides. She might also suggest that the alternative possibilities could provide the basis for an experiment; her attitude would be to "pick

one solution, try it for a while and see what happens."
She might assume temporarily the role of an educator
and instruct the aides in the administrative or clinical
theory or practice relevant to the situation. Here especially if she were dealing with a patient problem, she
would try to activate the aides' experience as mothers
and to characterize the patient's behavior as a developmental problem of a child at a certain age and then ask
the aides what they did with their children when they
behaved in such a fashion. She might also recognize that
the difficulty was arising out of the aides' inability to
make a decision because the problem was outside the
realm of their administrative or clinical function, or because it was beyond their therapeutic competence. In
such a situation the nurse would strive for a decision to
"talk it over" with the appropriate administrative or consultant personnel. If the conflict appeared to stem from
emotional or personality factors in the aides, her strategy
then was to recognize clearly and discuss these factors
in a supportive manner. Some final solutions available
to her were to suggest the status quo be maintained, that
is, the aides continue doing what they had been doing
until the conflict was settled; or she might advise the
aides not to decide and thus prevent any premature, im-
pulsive, or conflict-generating behavior. In each of these
strategies her primary goal was to support the assumption
of responsibility by the aide. In all of these courses the
nurse attempted fundamentally to convey a respect for
the aides' capacity to do the work with the patients and
to resolve their own conflicts. The issue was not primarily
a question of the aides' competence; the issue was rather
the manner in which the nurse could best support them
in their efforts at working through the problem.

3. "What do you do if you think an aide can't do the
job?" The problem here was to deal with what the nurse
conceived to be gross incompetence in an aide. An example of the way in which this question was answered
was reported by the supervisor of the ward nurse.

The ward nurse in one of our meetings reported to me
that she was seriously thinking of terminating Mrs. P, an
aide on the afternoon shift. She felt Mrs. P's judgment and

attitude were poor and she showed little insight or understanding into the goals of the project. The nurse was ready
to remove her from the ward. I felt that this would be an
irresponsible decision on her part and could create a difficult
situation on the ward. We discussed it and I suggested to
the nurse that she hold off on such a major step for a
while until she had a chance to consider all the possibilities
more fully, which she agreed to do. We discussed it on
several other occasions. It was felt that Mrs. P's confusion
was due to a lack of orientation to the project. Also discussed
were possible alternative solutions for handling the problem.
The *nurse's decision* after these discussions was to bring
Mrs. P on the morning shift for a period of about two
months where she could observe and work closely with her
in re-orienting her to project goals. It was clear in all these
discussions that the decision was the ward nurse's and that
I simply was expressing my reaction to the situation and
serving as a sounding board for the nurse.

Not all such situations were so readily resolved, however. It was eventually clarified that whenever the ward
nurse came to the responsible decision that an aide was
inadequate to the task, the nurse's recommendation for
dismissal or transfer would be acted upon.

The shift in the nurse's role from being responsible for
patients to being responsible for the aides was certainly
one of the most drastic changes of role attempted by the
project. Of all of those attempted, this change was perhaps the most difficult to bring about and took the long-
est to resolve effectively. The consensus among the staff
during the final year was that the new role did work. The
test of this role change was at the point where the ward
nurse felt that she no longer needed to be on the ward
eight full hours a day and was able to drop down to a
four-hour day at her own instigation. Above all, the new
role was most effective when, in conjunction with this
decision to partially withdraw, she also began to meet in
individual supervisory sessions with each of the aides. At
this point any aspect of the old traditional role concerned
only with observing aides and protecting the patients
from them had been thoroughly eliminated. It was now
obvious that the nurse's new task was to support and help
the aides function as responsibly as they could.

THE PSYCHIATRIC RESIDENT

By the end of the project the resident was present on the ward for six hours a week. Four of these six hours were taken up with partner meetings, that is, the daily meetings with a pair of the aide partners, the nurse, and the ward social worker. A fifth hour was taken up in a weekly team meeting of all of the ward personnel; and the sixth, in his meeting with the ward nurse, the ward social worker and a staff psychiatrist.

The crucial elements of the resident's role that finally evolved were, first, his skill in developing an atmosphere of openness and security in the partner meetings; second, his understanding of dynamic processes in the aide; and third, his appreciation of what came to be called "the parallel process." Parallel process, here, refers to the situation in which the same problem occurring in the aide's relationship to the patient is demonstrated in the aide's relationship to the consultant, and vice versa. Early in the project, for example, the aides seemed to be extremely over-protective of their patients. They were fearful of giving the patients too much freedom, and fearful of permitting their patients to make mistakes. They were angry when others in the hospital or elsewhere criticized their patients. However, this same protective attitude characterized the interactions of the consulting staff with the aides. They, too, were fearful of "letting the aides go," letting the aides make mistakes; they, too, were angry whenever anyone criticized the functioning of the aides. Just as the consulting staff was overprotective with the aides, so too the aides were overprotective with the patients. This parallel process manifested itself in many relationships. Conflict between two aide partners might be a symptom of one aide's conflict with a patient or a conflict between the consulting psychiatrist and the ward nurse. In its most basic form the parallel process was a manifestation of the work of identification, that is, that an individual will treat others as he is treated. It was primarily the psychiatrist who had an awareness, a working knowledge of this process, and who was trained in the techniques of using information about the parallel process.

It was this knowledge, then, that he as consultant brought to the partner meetings.

The skills described so far the psychiatrist brought to the ward by virtue of his training in psychiatry. A fourth, however, had to be gained through his experience on the project: he had to receive training to help the aides get distance and perspective from their treatment problems. In many respects this particular skill was an unusual one for a psychiatrist. Generally in his work with patients the psychiatrist's efforts are devoted to bringing feelings to awareness. He has a tendency to work toward lifting repressive mechanisms and helping people to become more aware of how they do feel. The assumption here is that once the patient knows how he feels he will then be able to act appropriately. On Ward H, however, the problems of feeling and emotion were somewhat different. Because of the nature of the aides, that is, their general feeling and action-oriented approach to life and because of the nature of the work situation, that is, a closed, intimate ward where they dealt with highly stimulating, provocative, disturbed patients, the aides' feelings were almost always readily available. Questioning and probing for underlying feelings were unnecessary. Generally all that was required was to acknowledge the aides' feelings. Once the feelings had been recognized by all concerned and their sources identified, the aides were able to have sufficient perspective and distance to plan appropriate therapeutic strategies. Certainly one of the first lessons learned by the psychiatric residents assigned to Ward H was that they were ill-advised to use an overly intellectual or probing approach to aides who were so little prone to disguise their feelings. Openness, clarity and perspective, rather than indirectness and subtlety, were most useful.

The major function then of the ward psychiatrist was not to tell the aides what to do but rather to create a climate that enabled the aides to understand how they might make most advantageous use of themselves with their patients.

As with the nurse, this role of the resident also underwent evolution. Throughout the course of the project the development of the resident's role centered around two major problems. The first of these was the problem of the psychiatrist functioning in the role of the consultant. For those aides who had previously functioned more traditionally there was a strong tendency to see the psychiatrist as a leader. Even though they were consciously aware of the new role for them in the project, much of their training and, under stress, their need for security, caused them to demand that the psychiatrist be an authoritative leader. For the psychiatric resident who was in his first year of training at Topeka State Hospital, functioning as a consultant provided almost insurmountable problems. For this individual who was entering a new specialty of medicine and was attempting to define for himself the role of the psychiatrist as a diagnostician and therapist, the role of consultant was confusing. Without an already well established identity as a psychiatrist it was difficult for him to deviate from the use of this role in direct treatment and to function as a consultant to others. For the advanced resident the major difficulties with the role of consultant came from an over-identification with the direct treatment model. If he were highly invested in the notion of treating through a one-to-one relationship with the patient, his capacity to gain any satisfaction from consulting with aides was diminished. Throughout the course of the project this consultant role appeared to be more comfortable for foreign rather than American-trained physicians.

The second major problem was that of psychiatric responsibility. The question frequently arose, "How can you be legally responsible for patients that you don't see?" Apart from the legal aspects of this question, it became evident that only through experience with this new role could the psychiatrist be sure that he could have an influence on the patient's treatment without seeing the patient. In time he could contrast this experience with his previous experience of directly treating chronic schizophrenics. Most of the psychiatric residents who had had experience on the project were convinced that they had more effectively carried out their responsibility toward the chronic schizophrenic patient serving as consultants to the aides rather than functioning in the direct treatment role or the role of the ward administrator.

THE SOCIAL WORKER

In the role that finally evolved the social worker provided two services. The first of these was termed "indirect service." Here the social worker attended the partner and team meetings. In these meetings it was her function to help the aides understand the dynamics of family life and the relationships between specific patients and their families. In these instances she would respond to the aides' questions about their contacts with the families. Here, she functioned as a consultant on family life and relationships. Her second function was that of direct service. Here, at the request of an aide, the social worker would work directly with the family. Since the aide's primary identification was with the patient and because the patient and the family were generally in conflict, it seemed wise to have a third person work directly with the families.

In the course of the development of this role a number of problems had arisen. Since the social worker had generally been used to communicating with professionals, it took some time before she was able to communicate and work with aides. Her second problem was the aides' attitudes toward the role of the social worker. At least early in the project the aides were determined to handle all of the family problems, even in those cases where it was technically impossible for them to do so. Consequently, the aides would seldom ask for direct service until a crisis with the family had erupted. It took time and the efforts of the entire consulting team to get the aides to ask for direct service from the social worker before a crisis arose. It was only after this situation had occurred a number of times that the aides appreciated the usefulness of the social worker in obviating such crises.

The third problem for the social worker was the aides' over-identification with the patients in their conflicts with relatives. This strong bias was especially present when the relatives happened to be the parents of the patients. This prejudice made it easy for the conflict between the patient and his parents to be displaced onto the aides and the parents and, once the social worker became directly involved, to be then displaced onto the social worker and the aides. The resolution of these problems required imaginative intervention on the part of the consulting team. In contradistinction to experience with parents, however, when the relative happened to be the patient's spouse the situation was usually different. In these instances the aides were able to identify not only with the patient but also with the spouse, and were able to work effectively.

In addition to her functions of providing direct and indirect services for the aides, the social worker was responsible as well for the development of the aides. She functioned in close conjunction with the ward psychiatrist and nurse, and attended a weekly meeting with them and a section staff psychiatrist to coordinate their work with the aides.

IN-SERVICE TRAINING PROGRAM

The in-service training program proved to be an essential part of the support system for the aides. As with the roles and other aspects of the project, this program evolved over a period of time. Initially the ward staff, that is, the nurse, the project directors, and the ward psychiatrist, acted as educators and instructed the aides in the theory of treatment. This dual role led to much confusion; the responsibility for education conflicted with the role of consultant, the primary function of these individuals. Because of their role as educators they found themselves subtly telling the aides what to do. The aides readily became aware of the inconsistency in the same individuals serving as both educators and consultants, as the ward professional staff was doing. (This is not to imply that these two roles are fundamentally incompatible. However, in view of the previous role confusion, the aide needs at this time required that a clear and perhaps somewhat arbitrary differentiation be made.) Because of this dilemma, at the beginning of the third year of the project, these two roles were separated and a group of educators who had neither administrative nor consultative responsibility toward the aides began to fill this role.

The staff based the content of the educational curriculum on the expressed needs of the aides. In this process the nurse was a key person in helping the aides to express their needs. Once a need for a particular type of content was expressed, an educator would be selected who was proficient in this area and who would meet with the aides weekly in a sort of seminar. In these seminars ideas would usually be presented by the leader and then discussion would follow. This plan worked particularly well when the material served as a stimulus for the aides to discuss their problems with patients. At times their spontaneous approach led to areas far from the material at hand, but usually much was learned from these excursions. The ward nurse generally sat in on these sessions and was very helpful in keeping discussions alive. She would ask questions when she felt that the aides did not understand, and also ask for clarification when the instructor would talk in an unclear or overly intellectual fashion. As much as possible, material was presented systematically. Since the levels system had come to be a core concept for the aides and one that they understood, information was presented and organized by means of this system. The discussions, however, were quite freewheeling. Throughout the course of the project the curriculum presented included information on the psychopathology of schizophrenia, group therapy activities with chronic schizophrenic patients, music and occupational therapy activities and skills, and the dynamics of family life.

The role of the educator then was to assume responsibility for the technical and cognitive competence of the aides. He did not give direct suggestions for treating specific patients; rather his function was to help the aides see and recognize underlying processes, and to apply them to treatment. In all instances, however, it was incumbent upon the seminar leader to follow the interests of the aides and to attempt to provide them with the information and stimulation that they wanted.

Crucial to the role of the educator was an open, informal, supportive relationship between him and the aides. This role came to have a special significance for the aides because it visibly demonstrated the staff's perception of them as capable of learning, thinking, and sharing information with professionals.

THE ROLES OF THE SUPERVISORS
OF THE WARD PROFESSIONAL STAFF

Each of the professionals working on the ward had a supervisor. These supervisors all met together weekly with the project directors. The principles guiding these supervisory relationships have been elaborated in the discussion of consulting supervision. The responsibility of this group was to maintain and reinforce a particular quality of relationship, viz., consulting supervision, throughout the project.

THE ROLES OF THE PROJECT DIRECTORS

In the final phases of the project the role of the project directors had been that of performing essentially a training function. They had trained the project staff at three successive levels. At first they had located themselves on the ward and had initiated the training of the aides. Later they had concerned themselves with the training of the ward professional staff; finally they directed the training of the staff who were responsible for the supervision of the ward professional staff. As each group reached an effective level of functioning, the directors withdrew and transferred their supervisory responsibility to the appropriate group in the administrative structure. Each withdrawal lessened the amount of time the project directors had to give for the maintenance of the project. Because the project members had been trained and had had an opportunity to experience and develop their roles, the directors were able to withdraw without jeopardizing the integrity of the project.

In the final phase of the project the directors' function consisted of attending a monthly meeting for all personnel. In this meeting they concentrated on the extent to which the project was achieving its overall goals. Problems at any level of the project were discussed; innovative efforts were explored. This meeting provided the directors with information on the degree to which the clinical, training and administrative aspects of the project were functioning in an integrated and valid manner. Apart from maintaining the viability and integrity of the project by virtue of their attendance at this monthly meeting, they were involved with evaluating the effects of the project at all levels.

SUMMARY

By the end of the fourth year then the project was working well. The original goals had been met through a continual elaboration of the original principles. This state of affairs, however, did not mean that there were not still extensive problems within the project. Certainly there were problems, especially in relation to the treatment of patients. These were the day-to-day, down-to-earth, grinding issues of treatment. The project staff, however, was pleased that the resolution of other issues allowed basic treatment problems to become the main focus of the program. A second problem area centered around the aides' concern about extending their responsibility into the community. The aides had developed a role for themselves. To some extent this role had been communicated throughout the hospital and there was acceptance for the aides' new way of functioning. They were less sure of such acceptance within the community. They were as yet still wary about extending themselves, they were fearful of the reaction they might cause. This is not to say that they did not extend themselves at all; however, they were less spontaneous and less enthusiastic about doing so. Finally, a major problem of the project was the concern over what was to happen when the project terminated. The project was funded up to September 1, 1964. A crucial question was, would the hospital be able to continue the project in its current form, would there be changes, would it be disrupted?

8

All Systems Go—The Ward Program—The Fourth Year

This chapter will be concerned with a presentation of the treatment rationales developed by the project, a sample day on the ward, and a case history of the treatment of a representative patient. The basic assumption of the project was that a *necessary* condition for the growth and improvement of the chronic schizophrenic patient was the presence of a spontaneous, fully functioning, consistent person who would be free to have an impact upon him. While a necessary condition, this was not assumed to be sufficient. During the project, a set of rationales evolved that permeated the aide-patient relationship. The presence of an aide using these rationales was seen as the necessary and sufficient conditions for treatment.

INTERPERSONAL RATIONALES

It is necessary to distinguish between what might be called interpersonal rationales that permeated all aide-patient interaction and those that were more specific to the meaning of given activities. The first of these interpersonal rationales was *a concern with identity*. For the most part chronic schizophrenic patients in general, and this was particularly true of those on the project ward, are unaware who they are in any real sense. They are frequently unaware of their existence and identity as bounded by a specific time, space, and body meaningfully related to the rest of the world. There is no cohesive sense of "I"-ness. This lack may be very gross, e.g., a patient actually may not be aware of his name, his age, where he was born, or that he is in fact on a mental hospital ward and has been there for twenty years. While this may be an extreme description, it was actually characteristic of many of the patients on this ward. Perhaps more characteristic, however, was that, while patients may be aware of some or all of these facts, they are not able to integrate meaningfully what they know to themselves. They may then be aware that they have been in the hospital for twenty years and state as much if asked, but the twenty years for them, with a distorted time sense, has a much different meaning than it has for others. The problem may reveal itself through the more physical aspects of the patient's identity. He may not, for example, be aware of the fact that it will be he who is scalded if he touches a hot radiator or steps into a tub of scalding bath water. So not only his name may be alien to him, but also his own body may lack a personal meaning for him.

Judy became particularly disturbed and upset over a period of time for what seemed to be an unexplainable reason. It was not until this behavior had persisted for several days that Mrs. R, her aide, became aware of a blister caused by an ill-fitting shoe. The blister no doubt hurt but Judy had been unable to localize this pain, either in terms of the part of the body affected or as physical pain.

It became a primary concern of the aides then to help the patients locate and define the internal experiences they were having as their own and to relate these experiences to their personal background, characteristic behavior, physique, reactions, feelings and talents.

Another rationale related to the first was that of *verbal development*. The aides tried diligently to attach words and labels to the patients' feelings, experiences, and body, and, when possible, to relate these to cause and effect. To show Judy that she had a blister, to tell her that what she was feeling from the rubbing of the shoe was pain and not a host of diffuse feelings was to attach a label useful to her. It gave these sensations differentiated meaning. Labelling provides an opportunity to transform inner experiences into verbal symbols and makes available to the patient a vehicle for communicating these experiences to others.

A further rationale was that of *intrusion* into the patients' inner experiences. Their experiences are chaotic and disorganized, with very few having meaningful rele-

vance to anything else. For the aide to be able to intrude
forcibly, constantly and insistently into this chaos was a
means of countering this disorganization. The aide's
presence in the patient's experiential world was to lend
something solid to the patient, something solid to which
other experiences could then be related. As the aide
forcibly reacted to the patient's behavior, feelings and
thoughts, there could develop in the patient a relevance
and an organization that could be anchored to the reality
of the aide's response. The feeling that Judy's blister
aroused in her could be given a name, but giving it the
name by itself would not help the situation for long. In
the case of Judy's blister the forcefulness, the intrusion
of Mrs. R helped her experience the pain in a differentiated manner; by putting salve on it, bandaging and
handling her foot, and talking to her about it she provided, not only the means of communicating this common experience between the two, but also the opportunity for intrusion. Because Mrs. R responded to the
blister, Judy came to experience *herself* as a person with
a blister.

The other major concern related to the treatment program was that of *graded expectations and responsibilities*
for the patients. Although all chronic schizophrenics, the
patients were not all the same. For each one there was
the need to assign responsibilities that were commensurate with her status and capacity. It was believed that
these expectations should always be at a somewhat higher
level than the one at which the patient was functioning.
Such responsibilities insured the patient's engagement
with the external world, enhanced her identity through
building skills and competencies, and provided the aides
with additional opportunities for intrusion.

ACTIVITY RATIONALES

The aides also utilized other rationales in the treatment of the patient. However, these were more closely
integrated into the daily rhythm of activities. After a
few months the aides gradually became aware that the
patients demonstrated different kinds of problems at

different times of the day. Consequently, activities began to evolve which were specific to problems manifested by the patients at these times.

MORNING—REORIENTATION

It soon became evident to the aides that most of their patients, upon arising in the morning, were somewhat disoriented and generally functioned at a lower level than they might later on in the day. For all humans, sleeping and night time are times when stimulation from the external world is reduced. Internal fantasies and reality merge in dream life. The individual is most passive and very much at the mercy of psychological forces over which he has little control. For most schizophrenics, whose equipment for dealing with this problem is already inadequate, early morning is a particularly difficult time. Sleeping and dreaming strain their already shaky facility for differentiating fantasy from reality, inner from outer stimulation. Upon awakening, their major need is for re-orienting themselves to the world, and re-experiencing themselves in a solid, valid way. It would be quite common, for example, to have a patient upon awakening make a statement about having seen her parents. She would talk about this as though it were real. The aide, however, would know that the parents had not actually visited nor had the patient gone home. After some discussion it would become apparent that the patient had dreamed of her parents during the evening and at this point was unable to distinguish between the dream and reality. Other patients, who had experienced frightening, anxiety-arousing dreams, would be extremely anxious, tense and fearful even though they would be unable to recall the dreams or unable to recognize that it was indeed the dream that had frightened them.

Apart from disturbances due to dreaming, the mere fact of awakening and reorganizing oneself presents problems for all patients. Consequently, early morning interactions and activities were focused upon *reorientation of the patient to his current life situation and reexperiencing of his own physical body and identity*.

The major emphasis was upon providing stability,

familiarity and routine within the context of physical experience of the self. Routinely, the patients were awakened at a definite time by the night shift aides. They were expected to attend to their personal care and to getting dressed in the intervening time between awakening and the arrival of the morning shift aides at 7:00 A.M. Following this period of dressing and personal hygiene the patients would go to breakfast. All the patients in a particular group would sit at the same table with their aide. After breakfast was over, each patient had definite housekeeping assignments. Blackboards and bulletin boards were present in all the groups' areas and listed the date, the assignments for each patient, and usually contained some statement about any deviations from these assignments. After assignments were finished there usually came a period of focused interest upon bodily experience and processes. It could include such activities as each member of the group weighing herself and listing her weight, the charting of menstrual periods, and doing physical exercises as a group. The aide was involved in each of these activities. Her efforts were to help the patient re-experience her own body and to recognize her physical self as the locus of her experience and as the pivotal point from which the world took on relevance. This routine of activities was typical of most mornings on Ward H, but there were deviations.

The personal style of each aide soon became evident in the way in which these activities were conducted, and in which activities were emphasized. Nonetheless, because each aide was relying upon her own personal style, her efforts with the group and her responses to individual patients remained consistent.

If one were to observe during the early morning period, both the stable routine and the individual style differences of the aides would become immediately manifest. At 7:00 A.M. all four of the aides would enter the ward together. As they walked down the ward, Mrs. Watts, upon nearing her group area, might call out, "Where are all my chickens?" She would glance through the group very rapidly, talking to the whole group at once, then singling out a single patient who was not appropriately dressed and asking the other patients what they thought about the way she was dressed. She would then ask the patient to get into something more appropriate. She would enter the aides' office to talk a few minutes with the night aides before they went off shift to see what had happened to her patients during the night.

Mrs. Stillman, on the other hand, would quietly enter her area and speak individually to most of her patients for a few moments, again commenting upon the way they were dressed, whether or not they looked upset, or asking how well they were feeling this morning. For her more regressed patients, she would go to them quietly, take them by the hand, ask them if they knew who she was.

Mrs. Ross would quickly gather her patients together in a group in her area, talking with them about their work assignments after breakfast, and commenting upon the fact that one of the patient's hair was uncombed and would ask her to go comb it. If one of her patients seemed very upset, she would talk with the patient for a few moments in an effort to assess the patient's capacity for control or regaining reality contact. If she felt that the patient was not going to be able to do this through the regular daily routine, she would ask the patient to go with her back to the seclusion rooms. If the patient were not too upset, she would simply ask her to stay in the seclusion room, closing the door but leaving it unlocked. If, however, the patient seemed on the verge of assaultive behavior or seemed extremely frightened of others, she might lock the door in an effort to provide the patient with a more bounded, secure environment. Upon leaving she would assure the patient that she would be back in a few minutes with a breakfast tray.

After seeing to the immediate needs of their patients, the aides would gather in the office, trading observations about patients with each other and the night shift aides, talking about what they expected during the day, talking with the nurse about what they intended to do, frequently joking and kidding one another.

Shortly before the arrival of the food cart for breakfast, Mrs. Jones, whose group was responsible for setting up the dining room for meals that month, would see to it that each of the patients was performing her assignment and that the dining room was prepared for breakfast. While her patients served, Mrs. Jones would observe closely to see that the patients received their fair share and that the prescribed diets were being observed. When one of her patients became sullen, angry or disruptive, Mrs. Jones would become annoyed with her, indicate her annoyance, and tell the patient that since her behavior was upsetting to the remainder of the patients she would have to eat out on the dayhall rather than with the group in the dining room.

In the meantime, Mrs. Ross prepared a tray for the patient she had earlier asked to go to seclusion, took the tray back to her, chatted a few moments, asking her if she was feeling any better and if she felt she would be able to leave seclusion soon. She then returned to the dining room and together with Mrs. Jones and Mrs. Stillman, sat with their respective groups and ate breakfast. During breakfast each of them would talk with patients about assignments that were to be done after breakfast. The aides might also work with the more regressed patients, many of whom had lost their awareness of taste, to improve their appreciation of taste. When syrup was poured over eggs, or bacon stirred into a bowl of fresh peaches, Mrs. Jones would react strongly to this inappropriate behavior, exclaiming, "For heaven's sake, Lila, you don't pour syrup on eggs." Mrs. Ross, on the other hand, might have the patient taste two different foods and try to get her to talk about the difference in taste.

Mrs. Watts, in her rapid assessment of the patients, had determined that, with the exception of one, most of them seemed to be functioning fairly well. She would tell her group to go ahead and eat. Taking Mona, the patient who was most disturbed, out to the dayhall, she began to work with her there. She and the patient would both stand before the large mirror on the ward. With both of them looking in the mirror, Mrs. Watts would point to herself and ask what her name was; then she would point to the patient and ask what the patient's name was. She might reach over, take hold of the patient's ear, and ask the patient whose ear that was. Or she might place her hand on the patient's forehead and ask the patient where she had placed her hand. Generally in all of this conversation she attempted to treat the patient humorously and lightly, and after a few minutes Mona would appear to be feeling better, would seem to be less troubled. At this point Mrs. Watts would suggest that they go into the dining room and have some breakfast.

While this technique worked well with Mona, with another patient Mrs. Watts might sit her on her lap, hold her almost as a baby, talk very quietly and softly to her in an effort to calm her. She might even sing softly to the patient for a while. Mrs. Jones, on the other hand, would handle the situation quite differently. She might put the patient to work at a task which would force her to attend to the task rather than to her own disturbing thoughts and feelings. Mrs. Jones indicated that she didn't really feel comfortable sitting the patient on her lap and therefore she wasn't going to do it.

After breakfast the aides then saw to it that each of their patients was performing her assignment. Mrs. Ross had June, one of her more intact patients, act as group leader. June was to see to it that the other patients were performing their assignments in a coordinated way. It was her function to insist that the assignments were done and to report to Mrs. Ross when they were done and which patients had cooperated and which had not. Mrs. Ross might then talk with, reprimand, or simply "bawl out" the patient who had not cooperated.

The more intact patients were generally assigned the more complex assignments, while the more regressed patients were given greater routine and simpler tasks to perform. No matter how regressed the patient might be, something would be expected of her in terms of ward work at this time. For example, one of Mrs. Stillman's patients, Alice, was an elderly woman who was extremely disoriented and regressed when the project began. She was almost mute, clutched nervously at a small rag doll which she kept with her at all times, and wandered aimlessly through the ward from door to door, trying each door in an effort to get out. After breakfast Mrs. Stillman would take a mop, ask Alice to put her doll down on a chair near them where Alice could still see it, take Alice's hands, put them on the mop handle, and hold them to it with her own hands. The two of them would begin to swing the mop back and forth in scrubbing motion. While doing this Mrs. Stillman would be talking to Alice about how heavy the mop felt, how much energy was needed to push the mop, whether or not Alice was really pushing and doing her part of the work, getting Alice to shake her arms and feel her muscles as they began to loosen up, and in general trying to help Alice experience her bodily sensations in the act of mopping and also what was going on between her and Mrs. Stillman. Mrs. Stillman went through this routine every morning for many, many weeks until finally she was able to take her hands away and Alice continued to mop alone. She was then able to expand the area which Alice mopped, and after a few months Alice was able to perform at least this simple assignment as her part of the group's work. The aides attempted to make these assignments as physically strenuous as possible in the hope that as the patients used their large muscles there would be more internal body stimulation.

During this period, while the patients were active and busy with their assignments, Mrs. Ross might return to the seclusion room to see if her patient was able to leave. The patient indicated that she was ready to leave seclusion and Mrs. Ross then asked her to take her tray back to the dining room so that the dishes could be washed. A few minutes later another patient reported to Mrs. Ross that the patient was now in the washroom washing her hair in one of the toilets. Mrs. Ross went back to the washroom, forcibly pulled the patient away from the toilet, took a towel and began drying her hair. She pointed out to the patient that if she felt she had some dirty thoughts this was not the way to get rid of them; you couldn't flush them out of your head, but that one had to keep busy and not think about them. She would then assign the patient to work with another patient at a rather demanding, distracting task.

Mrs. Jones would stay with her group, supervising them in their activities. She generally followed very carefully the way in which they performed their tasks, would frequently step in to indicate that the task was not done adequately, and demonstrate for the patient a better way of doing it. Mrs. Jones felt little compunction about being a demanding taskmaster with her more intact patients. Mrs. Stillman during this period would select one of her younger patients who seemed more in need of personal attention and would seat her before a dressing table, comb her hair, begin to talk to the patient, maybe tell her about her own daughter of similar age. She would talk about this daughter's preferences in hair style, cosmetics and clothing and compare the two. If the patient were more regressed, Mrs. Stillman might concern herself with forcing the patient to attend to her. She would insist on the patient handing her the comb, the brush, or the bobby pins at the appropriate time, would ask the patient to get them ready; but in this way keep the patient responding to her behavior and directions.

Generally during this period there was a great deal of physical contact between patients and aides. While Mrs. Jones might put her arm around the shoulder of an upset patient, Mrs. Stillman might sit beside her patient and hold her hand.

Frequently an aide's request to the patient to do her assignment would be met with a stubborn refusal. The aides' response was generally dependent upon their own attitudes and their assessment of a specific patient; for a more regressed patient, they might indicate certain behavior was expected of her. They could see she didn't want to do it this morning but perhaps she might tomorrow morning. However, they would leave the patient with the clear and definite feeling that patients were expected to do their assignments. With the more intact patient, Mrs. Jones, for example, would point out that work is something we all have to do; that if we do not work we do not eat, and the patient simply had to do her task. If the patient continued to refuse, Mrs. Jones might insist then that the patient would not have earned her lunch and therefore when lunchtime came she was not to eat. Mrs. Ross, on the other hand, might recognize that such a patient was angry because she had felt slighted in the morning by Mrs. Ross' inability to spend a few moments with her. Mrs. Ross would point out to the patient that she was angry. She explained that she hadn't had time to talk with her, but that she had not slighted her deliberately.

Certainly this might be seen as a representative morning. Still this group of activities was always subject to variations imposed upon it by the season, the day of the week, a reduction in the number of aides present because of illness or their need to relieve in another area of the hospital, or a disruption due to extremely bizarre behavior on the part of a patient. Suicidal attempts, assaultive acts or simply wild, uncontrollable behavior could disrupt the routine.

In summary then, the aide's major concerns in the morning were with helping the patient to re-establish physical contact with herself and with the world. Relying primarily upon activities that helped the patients to experience their own bodies, the aides used routine, stability and emphasis upon time and the usual daily activities basic to human life to orient the patients to reality.

MID-DAY—INDIVIDUALIZATION

In contrast to early morning activities, mid-day activities were directed toward helping the patient to differentiate herself from other patients and to respond to her more individual needs. While earlier the aides had relied upon routine and stability, the emphasis now was more upon the novel and the specific interests of the patients. Industrial assignments were particularly valuable for the more intact patients for whom a job downtown was being planned. Generally these industrial assignments would be related to the type of work that the patient was seeking. Patients who were going to apply for jobs as waitresses might be assigned a job in the hospital canteen waiting on tables or behind the counter. An aide frequently went to the various work areas where her patients were assigned to chat with them and their supervisors, and in general to get some feeling as to their progress and their problems. Those patients who were less intact but seemed to need strong reality intrusion might be assigned jobs such as laundry work. Since the laundry worked on a semi-assembly line basis, the patient would be forced in a sense to attend to her particular task. As sheets came off the mangle they had to be quickly taken hold of and folded so that the very work, in and of itself, was of an intrusive nature. Those patients who were not on industrial assignments would remain on the ward and would generally engage in activities with the aides, such as sewing, fixing up their own ward areas, making cookies, studying, practicing their typing, or engaging in group therapy activities. For many of the patients it had been years since they had cooked or had much to do with the kitchen. Volunteers were asked to come onto the ward and conduct cooking classes for selected patients. Other patients who seemed to need the quiet or for whom the aides had been unable as yet to determine a treatment plan, were permitted to rest, sit quietly, read, or write letters.

It was also at this period of the day that many spontaneous activities would come about. In the springtime the patients might plan a garden, select a plot of ground, and plant flowers or vegetables. Frequently during the spring and the summer there were plans for picnics; on a given day a group would go to one of the city parks, roast wieners, wander to the zoo, or simply relax in other ways. Other groups made tours of the local phone company, a dairy, or other local industries. For many patients, simply wandering through a grocery store and checking the current prices of food was a novel experience.

After the ward activities had been completed and Mrs. Jones had sent out those patients who were assigned to various adjunctive therapies or industrial assignments, she might gather the remainder of her patients around the record player to dance the "hokey-poke." Mrs. Jones liked dancing herself and consequently used it frequently with her patients. She would gather the patients in a circle and start the record. One would hear her calling out to a specific patient, "Come on, Janet, it said to put your left arm, not your right arm; that is your right arm you've got in; put in your left arm. For heaven's sake, Mary, it said shake it all about." She might then stop the group, go up to Mary, take her arm, shake it vigorously and indicate this was the way it was to be shaken; not simply a mechanical, stereotyped turning. After this, one of the patients might ask Mrs. Jones if she would jitter-bug for them and Mrs. Jones, if she felt inclined that morning, might begin to teach one of the patients who seemed to be interested to jitterbug. She and her patients might then go to their own group area and sit, have cof-fee and chat for a while. Or she might leave them to their own activities while she went back to the office, did some charting, talked to the other aides, or simply relaxed. After a period of time she might return to her patients and they would take up work on a project in their own group area.

Most of the aides had become interested in some sort of group therapy activity. They were well aware that sit-ting around talking and the exploration of feelings were not particularly useful to this group of patients. However, group activities that were oriented toward dealing with the patient's body image problems, the experience of themselves and the experience of one another, were felt to be fruitful. Consequently, most of the aides were able to initiate some sort of group activity. Each of them used whatever particular set of skills or interests she had as a vehicle for the activity. Each met with an individual from the staff who had had experience with group activity to discuss group work with her patients.

Some of the aides became concerned with the more long-term patients who had not had any real contact with money for a long time. Generally most patients did not have money but were issued hospital can-teen books. These were books of tickets which could be traded for goods at the hospital canteen. Mrs. Watts did not feel this plan was realistic so instead of purchasing books for her patients she gave them money, pointing out that if they were to go downtown this is what they would have to do. Mrs. Watts liked to get her patients off the ward at this time. The availability of money in her group facilitated trips downtown. She would go shopping with some of them and buy shoes or clothes. Her group might also go to a nearby park and visit the zoo. She would often take patients with her on errands, or to visit other patients in the group who were on industrial assignments.

Mrs. Stillman liked to work with her patients on an individual basis; she would spend this period of the day talking and working with one patient at a time. The remainder of her patients were permitted to leave the ward on a group ground pass. These patients would leave the ward as a group with one of the patients in charge and would be on their own to go to the hospital canteen, wander about the grounds, and talk with other patients.

Mrs. Ross had a knack for crafts so she might work with patients during this time, e.g., making a mosaic table top for their group area. The activity would be interrupted when Mrs. Ross might be called to the phone by the patient whose assignment was to answer the ward phone. During this time of day relatives would frequently call to ask about patients or to talk about weekend home visits. Mrs. Ross would discuss the possibility of a pass with the relatives, and arrive at a decision about its feasibility.

In their conversations with relatives each aide used her own approach. For example, one of Mrs. Watts' patients was a young girl who, though very delusional, had been permitted to go home for weekend visits. After one of these visits, her mother called Mrs. Watts and began to enumerate some of the patient's delusions about her mistreatment at the hospital. Mrs. Watts responded by indicating that both she and the mother knew the girl was ill, that she was frequently unable to distinguish between her imagination and reality, and wondered if the mother really believed everything the girl had told her. The mother responded, "Well, I'm her mother and she's my daughter and I certainly should know when she's lying," at which point Mrs. Watts agreed with her and indicated that since she was her mother and seemed to feel the girl should be believed, that perhaps it would be best if the aides were to take their lead from her and also believe what the girl told them. Mrs. Watts then added, "Of course, last week when she came back from home she told us that she had had intercourse with her father."

It was also at mid-day that most job-finding activities were undertaken. The aides and patients would look through the daily paper for jobs, and an aide might answer an ad by phone to discover what type of work was required, where the job was located, and to get some understanding of the employer's attitude toward mental patients. If it appeared a possible opportunity for the patient, the aide and the patient would discuss the job, and the patient would go for an interview. Usually the aides were very anxious about the patient's appearance before the job interview. They would attend to the way the patient was dressed, and how her hair was combed. They would talk about and almost role play the employer-patient interaction. Sometimes the aide would take the patient to see the employer; on other occasions the aide might go first and talk with the employer before sending the patient. Other patients were encouraged to do most of their job finding on their own. When some patients had found a job, the aide might spend a number of hours a day on the job to support the patient's acclimation to the work situation.

Anyone walking on the ward during the late morning hours would find very few patients there. Most were either on group ground passes, in activities, or at industrial assignments. The few who did remain were usually being worked with fairly actively. Just before noon most patients would return to the ward, the dining room would be set up for lunch, the patients and aides would eat, and the dining room would be cleaned up again.

Early afternoon was usually the most inactive time. Many of the patients would rest for a while, write letters, or read. Some would return to their jobs or industrial assignments. Others would be out on individual ground passes, away from the hospital at work, job-finding, or shopping. The aides were usually busy at this time in the office, charting the day's activities, possibly planning for tomorrow's activities, or meeting with the partner aide on the PM shift and the consulting staff to discuss their nine patients.

Throughout this mid-day period then the primary emphasis was upon an individualization of the treatment program and responsiveness to the patients' specific needs, talents, and problems.

At 3 o'clock the morning shift aides would leave and the PM shift aides would arrive for work. Again there was a few minutes overlap which would enable the aide partners to talk with one another about the patients' behavior and to consult with each other on treatment plans. This

occurred every day in addition to the more extensive discussions that each aide pair had once a week when they
met with the consulting staff.

SOCIALIZATION AND LABELING

The PM shift's primary concern with the patients was
socialization and verbalization. While the morning activities related to the patients' involvement in the work-
a-day world, the PM shift was primarily concerned
with leisure time, socialization, and the development
of verbal skills. As with most people, the patients' late
afternoon and evening hours were generally dedicated
to leisure, a review of the day, and to socialization with
their family or friends. During the earlier part of the day
the patients had been oriented to the world and to themselves as much as possible and individual needs had been
answered. Usually by late afternoon the patients were as
intact as was possible. Consequently, the PM shift tried
to help patients consolidate in conversations what had
occurred during the day. In addition, the PM aides gave
special emphasis to the socialization process.

There was great attention given to social activities such
as visiting, playing cards and other games, attending hospital evening activities, leaving the ward with volunteers,
going downtown for recreational activities, and, on a
weekly basis, inviting patients from the male sections of
the hospital to the ward for a ward social.

The aides spent time with the patients on an individual basis in which the patients' worries and experiences
of the day were discussed. Group therapy activities tended
to be much more verbal than those conducted by the day
aides and those patients who were able were encouraged
to form groups, such as a patient ward council or a "gripe
group," wherein the patients aired their complaints about
the ward.

On a typical day, after chatting with the AM aides,
the PM shift would go out on the dayhall and visit
with the patients. The differences in individual style
were again apparent in the PM aides; they would wander
through the ward talking with various patients, seeing to
it that they were carrying out their assignments, remind-

ing patients to write letters home, talking with the patient on an industrial assignment about her work, talking with the patient who was working downtown about her job and how she was to budget her money. In late afternoon dinner would be served. Again each of the patients had assignments for the preparation of the dining room and cleaning up afterwards. The PM shift aides would also eat with the patients and during this period there would ordinarily be some discussion about their evening activities.

Mrs. Wash frequently liked to take her patients downtown. During the evening she might talk with them about going roller skating. If the majority of the group agreed, they would go downtown. One or two patients might be too ill and would be left behind in the care of one of the other aides. Another might refuse to go because she was not interested or too frightened. In general Mrs. Wash would try to convince the patient that she needed this kind of experience and that it would be good for her to go. If the patient did not seem to resist too strongly, she would take the patient with her. On occasion, former group members who had gotten jobs and moved into apartments downtown would be called and asked if they would like to go roller skating with the group. They would then get into Mrs. Wash's car, pick up the former patients on the way, and would go roller skating together. On the way back to the hospital the group might stop off at the apartment of one of the former patients, have coffee, chat a while, and return to the hospital by 10:00 in the evening.

Mrs. Taylor, on the other hand, would spend a good deal of her time talking individually with patients, trying to help them work through problems. One of the patients in her group, Jean, was a young attractive girl in her twenties who had progressed enough to take some evening courses at the local university. While there she met a young man who became interested in dating her. She approached Mrs. Taylor with this problem. Mrs. Taylor talked with her and also with the morning aide about the appropriateness of Jean's dating. Both aides decided, after some discussion, that this kind of experience would be useful for Jean's recovery as long as the dating was well supervised. Consequently, Mrs. Taylor conveyed to Jean that she could date if the young man would come out to the hospital first and talk with Mrs. Taylor, which he did. She felt, in her own assessment of him, that he was reliable and indicated to him what the limitations were on Jean's dating. She indicated that Jean would have to be back on the ward at a certain time, that before they went out he would have to come to the ward, pick her up, and indicate where they were going. The young man agreed to all these conditions and Mrs. Taylor followed closely Jean's relationship with him. She and Jean would spend many evenings talking about Jean's experience in the relationship and her fears about it, especially some of her concern about sexual feelings.

In their discussions Mrs. Taylor's interest was to get Jean to verbalize her feelings and help her label them. Once the feeling was labeled, Mrs. Taylor would then talk with Jean about how she handled similar feelings when she was a young girl, what some of the issues were, and what behavior was appropriate. In many of these discussions Jean would express her worries about her feelings for the boy and what they meant. She had fears of losing his attentions, doubts about their personal attractiveness, and feelings of social inadequacy. Mrs. Taylor would try to help her label and understand these feelings, indicate what feelings she needed to control and how, and what ones she should feel free to express spontaneously. Mrs. Taylor spent a number of evenings teaching Jean to dance, and otherwise gain the social skills she needed in these new relationships.

Mrs. Nelson's interests, however, were primarily with some of the older women on the ward. Her more youthful patients generally attended the hospital's evening activities but Mrs. Nelson felt that some sort of supervised social activities on the ward were important for the older patients; consequently, she initiated a "social group." Older male patients were invited each Sunday evening for cards, dancing and refreshments. During this time Mrs. Nelson would observe the group closely and later on would try to talk with each of her patients so that she might provide feedback on their behavior and try to help them learn appropriate social skills.

Frequently the more intact patients on the ward were encouraged to go downtown in the evening unaccompanied by an aide. At such times patients might be extremely critical of each other's behavior. It was obvious that each patient group was setting its own standards; frequently, a group might refuse to have patients go with them who exhibited bizarre, pathological behavior at the hospital. Much to the surprise of the other patients and the aides, these patients frequently recognized the difference between being downtown and being at the hospital. Downtown their behavior was extremely appropriate although they seemed to have no qualms about bizarre behavior when at the hospital.

On occasion one of the aides might receive a call from a former patient who was now living downtown and wanted to discuss one of her problems. Occasionally, if the aide felt it was a critical event in the patient's life, she would leave her group in charge of another aide and go to the patient's home or apartment.

Usually most of the patients would have returned to the ward from evening activities, work, or a trip by 9:30. While most of them were preparing for bed, a few patients might gather in the kitchen, pop popcorn or make punch. The aides and patients might all have a snack before the patients were off to bed.

The duty of the evening shift was to help the patients consolidate the gains of the day by labeling their experiences, symbolizing them, and talking about them. In addition, their efforts were directed towards initiating and fostering a social sense in the patient and helping the patient to recognize her need for social competencies, skills, and interactions with others.

The foregoing material has been descriptive of a day on Ward H. In an effort to provide the reader with the flavor of the long term treatment process as experienced by the project aides, the following material, taken from a presentation by one of them, is offered. It reflects her perception of the project, and her work over a four-year period with a representative patient.

On our project, the No. I level was the patient who had no experience of body functions. This was a patient who wouldn't wash, wouldn't comb her hair, didn't know who she was and really didn't care. This is where we had to get in there, get them out of the corner, get them to a mirror, show them their nose, their eyes, who they were, who I am, and let them know that they have to function. We had to keep pushing to them—who you are, where you are at, where your nose is at, where your hands are at; all these boundaries.

We also had a music therapist. When she came on the ward she would teach the aides to play records with the patients, make them march—anything to motivate them. Also the OT worker would teach us to get the ones who knew how to knit, get them started knitting or sewing or even to painting with their fingers. You know, we had some patients who would play in feces and instead of having them play in feces I would rather have them play in paint any day. So they would finger paint. They would work their fingers with the finger paints. We had clay throwing. We would put them in seclusion and just let them throw clay up against the walls. Sometimes we would just sit in there with them just to let them know that we were there, you know, to even be along beside them. That would give them some help.

The combative patients we felt like if we would keep them motivated with something they liked to do, like playing basketball or even running up and down the halls, this would spend more of their energy. They would spend more energy by playing basketball and less energy trying to break our necks. So if they kept motivated they would be tired. So in this way they spent their energy doing something worthwhile. So we were always busy.

Then when they got to Level III where they would try to function and try to know who they were and what ward they were on, and what day it was, what year it was, then that is when we would put them in groups, we would take them in our cars, we would take them swimming, we would take them skating, we would take them to movies, all these different places to show them how people on the outside functioned.

Now at first we always went with them but as they gradually showed us that they were progressing we would put them in groups of four or five and let them go by themselves because this way they would get unattached from us because after working this close they would get so attached to us that there had to be a breaking point where they would go by themselves. So we would give them a ground pass and we would give them a special time to come back and if they didn't come back we would have to run all over Topeka looking for them, which we did a lot of times. The hospital is just about a half mile from the miniature golf course. We would let them go play miniature golf or we would put them on the bus and let them go to a movie, anything that would get them off the grounds as much as possible.

When they would reach Level IV we would work with them on trying to get a job. Now in the problem of getting a patient a job, all you have to do is send a patient down town, if they tell someone they are from Topeka State Hospital, that's it. They are sent back. They won't hire mental patients. Now some places will break the barrier and they will give them a chance, but most of the time when we first send our patients out they would be to a certain level but they just couldn't hold their jobs yet so then they would fail. So they would have to come back to the ward and start all over again and try again. So over a period of four years you can imagine the patients falling back and us trying to build them up again and trying to get them another job. But we kept on trying.

Now once they got to a job level and they would hold this job for six months to a year then we would think about dismissing them because we felt if a patient could hold a job and stay on Level IV, you know, they should be able to get a job and keep it and get an apartment and stay out. Now our belief was that if you take a patient and you put the patient back in the environment that the patient came out of, the patient will get sick and return to the hospital. So the best way to do it if you want your patients to stay out is to change the environment and put them in a better environment and their chances of staying out of the hospital will be much better than to put them back in the very same environment that they came out of when they were admitted to the hospital. So this is the reason we would let the patients stay on the job six months, save their money, and then we would attempt to try to find them an apartment. We would go along with them to find the apartment, we would help them get their dishes and their sheets and get them started at it. The whole group would do this, not just me. This was just too much work for me to do all by myself. I would take my nine patients with me to do it too. We would all move. I would use my car; we would just load it up. We would load it up, move the patient in, and the last thing I would tell her was, "Please don't come back, stay out!" After she was dismissed we would ask her to come back once a week to see us. This was just in order for us to see how she was functioning because if she came back on the ward, after working with a patient this close for this many years, you would know if she was slipping or not. So she would come back on the ward and talk to us, and we would ask her about her job or where she would go at night when she got off work; just different things to feel her out to see how she was functioning on the outside. This was kept up for, oh gosh, six months. If she didn't come in we would go to her. We would go over there and visit her just to see how she was keeping her apartment up, you know, to keep track, to make sure that she would stay out, to give her some support, because when you get patients in the hospital and they live there fifteen years they need some support from somebody; they need to know that there is somebody there who really cares. So we kept following it up.

On one occasion I dismissed a patient and when the group went skating I went by and picked up the patient and took her skating along with the group although she had been dismissed from the hospital, because she wasn't doing anything but sitting there looking at the four walls anyway. And so I took her along to the skating rink and we went skating and, of course now, skating was a good activity for the patients because if you don't keep your balance on skates you are going to fall, you know. So I enjoyed putting them on skates just to see what they were going to do. By a miracle nobody broke their bones; they got a little sore but no bones were broken. When we went to take this particular patient back home to let her out she didn't want us to go; she wanted to go back to the hospital with the group because she felt closer to the group. But we always followed up on our patients when we dismissed them. Of course now, I could talk all day on this because this was a four year project, but I am not going to do that. I am going to give you an example of what we did for one patient. This way you will know almost how our day went with almost all the patients because we tried to do the same for every one of our patients.

This particular patient who was admitted to our hospital had been an aide before she got sick. She had worked with most of us. She had been a quiet and withdrawn person in the first place and didn't have much to say. And, of course, being married to the nice boy that she was married to, made her more withdrawn because he was a playboy and he didn't want to provide for his family. He didn't want to provide enough food and they had five children, and, of course, when she had the last baby she had to quit work. So this really made her withdraw. He wasn't providing for the family adequately. She became catatonic. She was a chronic schizophrenic catatonic.

When she was admitted this was the state she was in. We couldn't get any response out of her; she would not talk to any of us. She had worked with some of us and still wouldn't talk to us. She would sit in the corner and drool at the mouth, eat very little, and just not even function. She would just sit there for hours if you would leave her sit there. She would just rock back and forth and just sit.

Well, the first thing was to give her ECT (electric shock treatment). When we first started electric shock treatment we thought that did marvelous because she kind of roused, you know. But in thirty days' time we would leave one day and the next day we would come back and she would be the same old way. The electric shock treatment would only keep her up about thirty days for the most, and then she would slip right back on us like she had never had anything. This kept up for about two or three months and we figured why in the world was this patient climbing up the ladder and then slipping back again right before our eyes, you know, over night.

Well, she was being visited by her family, her darling mother; she was being visited by her minister who would talk religion all the time he was there; and she was being visited by her darling husband which hadn't changed one bit. So we decided that it was the family. We decided we would try to see if it was the family that was making this patient regress. So we cut off all visits from her family. We really upset the family. They were running down to CNO (Central Nursing Office) and everywhere else. How could we just cut off their visits to their relative? How in the world did aides have this much authority? But, anyway, they didn't get to see the patient.

The mother was told to report to our social worker and our social worker would work out something with her and she could have therapy with the social worker and when she was able, or when Helen would be able to see them and cope with the visits, she could see them again. But until she was able to, the family would have to stay away. From this point we started working with Helen. Now Helen was slow progress because, as I said, she would improve and she would slip back.

She was the patient that we took to the State Fair one

time, we took all nine of our patients there, and we had to pull her around. And if anybody has ever been to a State Fair and pulled a patient around with nine others, you would know just what I was talking about. It was tiring. But there she was, drooling and her head bowed, but we pulled her around; we kept her going. We took her to the State Fair, we took her on a camping trip to a cabin by a lake.

I will have to tell you about this experience because it was quite a dilly. I had a partner, Mrs. Watts, who worked with Helen first. She worked with Helen real close first and she was an awful good aide, very attentive. She expired in September of 1964. She would be here today if she were able. But we went on this camping trip and one of our patients decided she would take a swim in the lake. So we were trying to keep track of all nine patients and we just happened to turn our heads and one of our patients had jumped in the lake. Of course, Mrs. Watts, she grabbed her heart and said, "Oh my gracious, Ward H has lost a patient." And, of course, I started laughing and that made Mrs. Watts kind of mad, you know. We called everybody, boats and everything, to get the patient. She swam and then she got out of the water and walked on back up into the cabin, changed her clothes and came on out. Of course, Mrs. Watts was still standing there holding her heart, but she could swim better than any of us. And of course, Mrs. Watts afterwards when she was telling it, particularly when we got back, she laughed then too after the patient was safe and everything. But we had a very nice time at the lake. The patients enjoyed it. I don't think Helen even knew she was there at the time, but she was there. We stayed over night and we went back to Topeka the next day.

Now we did all sorts of things like the camping trip and taking them to the Fair. We did all these with all of our nine patients. We had the feeling that we would never take the good ones and leave the sick ones because we felt just as close to our regressed patients as we did to the ones who were functioning good. The Level IV patients we tried to have them help us take care of the Level I patients. In this way the group was in harmony and were all functioning together.

Now back to Helen. Working with her, we cut out the ECT and said we would just have to work with her on our basis, you know, intrude upon her, keep her moving, and stimulate her. Along with this we started her on Stelazine. Now here Stelazine gets credit but I really think our working close with her is what really did it. We started her functioning, we had to show her body awareness, we had to keep her going. We ran her up and down the hall, I would make her play basketball. At first when we started throwing the ball at her she would just let the ball bounce up against her and it would just bounce right back to me. It was just a hopeless case. Sometimes I would say I just give up. But we kept on going and we kept on pushing her and she finally started to rallying and functioning.

Now when we first started we would fix her up. We would comb her hair for her and put on make-up for her and dress her up and show her in the mirror how she looked dressed up instead of with her hair all over her head and every way. She would let me do this; she would wear this make-up. But as she started getting better the real Helen came out. She was a religious woman and she didn't believe in make-up. So as she came to the level she started not wanting me to put make-up on her. Of course, I argued back and forth with her. You look better with make-up than without make-up. But, of course, she informed me that she was Helen and I was Mrs. Wash. She had gotten to the level where she told me who I was and who she was. So I said if this woman really believes in this, there was no sense in me trying to put make-up on her if she really didn't believe in this. So she started fixing herself up but she would not wear make-up and she doesn't wear it today.

Along with this, as she started progressing, she started going to the church out on the grounds. We would let her go to church out on the grounds on Sundays. Then eventually she asked us "Would you let me go to my church?" We were kind of leery of this because at the church here is mamma and here is the minister and here is darling husband. He will be somewhere around. He will take time off to be around! We held a meeting to discuss this—should we let her go. But we had to know if this would make her slip back; we had to know what effect it would have on her to really see her family. So we let down the barriers. We let mamma visit her once a month. We let husband come and visit her, and then we eventually let her go to her own church.

Now she would slip back but not as far as she did at first. She would get depressed and she would sit there with her head down, but then all we had to do was to start motivating her and talk to her a little bit and everything, and she never would slip back down as far as she had at first. So, therefore, we knew that she was improving slowly.

With this, we let her start going to her church every Sunday and she would visit with her mother and she would visit with her husband.

But in the meanwhile, dear husband, they had asked him to go to the Out-Patient Clinic because he was sicker than Helen. So he was admitted to Topeka State Hospital. Well, in the meanwhile he saw Helen; you know, when both of them were in the hospital there was no way in the world we could keep them apart. When we let Helen go to the canteen, there was dear Louie. He informed her that the only reason he was put in the hospital was because she was there, and he was there to support her. And he really had her believing this; he wasn't sick; the only reason he was in the hospital was for her. And she believed everything he said.

So we had Louie there on the men's section and Helen there on the women's. We were trying to get Helen well and here is Louie being just as sick as he wants to be. But he is convincing everybody on the ward that he is not sick. But anyway, along with Louie being there, we still kept on with Helen. We got her to the point that we said we would try to see if she could hold a job. The first two jobs failed.

Helen had lived in Topeka quite a few years before she came into the hospital, but with her withdrawal and everything she had forgotten her way around Topeka. But, anyway, with us sending her out on this job we didn't really realize how far she had forgotten, you know, Topeka surroundings. So we sent her out on this job one morning and we were all enthused, she is starting her job. We put her on the bus. About an hour later the woman called and said, "Where is the girl who is supposed to work for me?" I said, "We sent her; she is supposed to be on her way somewhere." Helen was standing on the street corner waiting for a bus for an hour that she had never caught! She was still standing there! She had lost her way and she had become confused and she didn't know where she was going. So, therefore, she was just standing there in one spot. Of course, we got her and brought her back and we started all over again. We took her in our car and drove her around Topeka to get her familiar with the surroundings in Topeka so they would gradually come back to her where everything was at. We got a break and a nurse from another hospital wanted someone to babysit for her. Now she worked with these kind of people so she understood them. So this was a break for Helen really, and so she took Helen. At first Helen worked for her during the day time and came back to the hospital at night.

Dear Louie, in the meantime, had gotten paroled. So when this woman finally asked if Helen could stay at her house and babysit, you know, off the grounds and come in week-ends to see us, we said this would be a good idea. We would know whether she could tolerate this. So we agreed to let her go and stay at the woman's house. In the meantime Louie is out on parole and he is running over to the house and he is calling, and everything, to get Helen upset. But Helen wants Louie. We couldn't say anything against Louie because Helen loved Louie and there wasn't any sense in us even arguing about that. She wasn't going to divorce him.

We decided that if we were going to get this girl well and if she was going to stay well, we would just have to forget about Louie being no good because she was going to accept him just as he was. So we put our heads together and said now she is out on this job, they have five children. Now when she got sick her mother took care of these five children at first. But then her mother was taking care of these five children and she just couldn't stand it. The baby went to a foster home in Topeka while the four other children were sent to Louie's sister, so that separated the kids. So we had to plan how to get Helen well enough to function and take care of her kids and how was Louie going to fit into the picture, and how were we going to get a new environment for Helen instead of letting her go back to the same drab house with hardly no furniture and no food.

In the meanwhile when Louie had been in the hospital he was a veteran. So he had been receiving money. Along with him receiving money, as long as he was a patient at Topeka State Hospital he had to have a guardian, so the guardian had been receiving his checks and he had been saving them. So here with Helen working we had saved Helen's money. So therefore we put two and two together and we said well, if we can get this together, this money together, maybe we could get them a place to stay and start a new environment for Helen. But first we had to talk to Louie to see what he was going to do about the situation.

At this point we had to call Louie and ask him if he would come and talk with us. Of course, he pulled our leg. Boy, he was going to be a model husband, he was going to work hard, he was going to help his wife stay well. And so at this point we said, "Okay, Louie, if you are going to cooperate then all we have to do is try to find where are you going to live." Now in Topeka they have a housing project where you pay rent according to what you make, your salary. So we got together and we went and found a house that they could pay rent according to what Louie made, as long as Louie kept his job.

Their rent wasn't too high but then we had the problem of a bare house with no furniture. So we said maybe the guardian or Louie would go along with furnishing the house and getting the sheets and the dishes, because they didn't have anything to go along with. So we got busy and we had to talk to the guardian and we had to talk to Louie. In the meantime Louie is telling us he is agreeing to all this and he thinks this is just wonderful. Then he goes to his guardian and says he doesn't want his money spent this way; he wants a new car! He would rather have a new car than buy all this furniture. So there we are. Here we are blocked again. Helen, we think, is well enough to get out and try to start but we don't know where to start because dear Louie has told us one thing and has told the guardian another. So then we sat for two weeks wondering what we were going to do and the guardian decided that he was going to go on and help us and get the furniture and get them started, whether Louie wanted to or not. In the meanwhile Louie said, "I'm going along; I'm going along with it; if my guardian says that, I'll go along with it." So, okay, we start the ball rolling.

We went with them to pick out the furniture and we got all their towels and their dishes, everything. We had to go with Helen to the house, we had to help her clean the house up and hang her curtains, and we just stood by her and helped her in all this. In the meanwhile we had asked the social worker to help with the foster parents to see if Helen could get the baby back. The foster parents agreed that if Helen was well enough to take her baby, they were willing to let her have her baby.

Now Helen was discharged in February of '63, so this made her able to take her baby first but she had to wait on the other four children because they were in school and they had gotten weaned away from Helen whereas the baby . . . a baby will accept you quicker than older kids will after they have been away from you so long. So then we had to start, before we dismissed Helen we had to send her to visit her children on the week-ends so that they could get used to each other again, to see how Helen would react after seeing them. So we sent her and she spent the week-end by herself, we thought, without Louie. But Louie went along anyway! Louie was always around. She went to see her children which, at first we said well, this girl has reached a point where she knows us, where she is holding a job, but she doesn't mention her kids too much so maybe she doesn't want her kids back. But she started babysitting and she would come to my home, which I have five children —if you don't like children there is no sense in being around my house—she liked my children, and we felt well, she likes everyone else's children she is bound to want her own; she just hasn't mentioned them; she felt in herself that she wasn't going to get them so I guess she felt she wasn't going to mention them. But after we sent her to visit her children she started talking about them. She wanted them. She started writing them letters and they would write back and forth to her. So the month that we discharged her she started in her new home and her new surroundings with her one baby; she got her other children in June.

Of course, dear Louie had gotten an awful good job and with God's grace he kept the job, but dear Louie never did change. He still was a lady's man, and still outtalks everybody else, and he still was very, very sick but he was dismissed from the hospital and he still is dismissed. Helen got to Level V. I feel that if she hadn't gotten to Level V she would never have been able to cope with Louie.

Now when Mrs. Watts passed away, Helen was awful close to Mrs. Watts because Mrs. Watts had worked with her since the time she entered the hospital. Helen sung a solo at Mrs. Watts' funeral, and also she had written a letter that she read at Mrs. Watts' funeral telling how close she was to Mrs. Watts, how attentive Mrs. Watts was, how she really appreciated the love, the understanding, the attention that she had given all those many years, that she realized that without her guidance she never would have been able to get this far in life. This was very inspiring to me because I happen to have been there and she didn't break down once. She read the letter, she sung the solo beautifully.

At this time she is still out of the hospital. She is functioning real well; she is raising her five children; and Louie is still the same. As I say, he hasn't changed one bit. But I talked to her and told her that I was coming to talk to you and she told me to have a nice trip and she said that with God's help Louie might change one of these days. Now, this girl is deeply religious and she believes this, but I don't know.

In working with this project we had some trying times,

along with the good results. In any project you will have
trying times. You are going to make mistakes. As for me,
I made quite a few of them. I know we had one case where
the patient was all ready to leave the hospital. We had her
packed up and everything. Her family came after her and
by the time they walked in the door she had regressed so
far back that we couldn't even get her out the door. We
unpacked the bag. Her family went back home and the very
next night when I was on duty she was trying to elope.
And I looked at her and I said, "Do you really want to
elope?" I said, "Well, I tell you what, I am going to open
this door and I am going to let you out this door. If you
want to elope this bad, you go on." Now, of course, I
knew she wasn't going to elope because she was supposed
to be dismissed and she didn't want to go. She eloped! I
spent all night running after that patient. I called our
doctor three or four times, got him up out of bed, and come
to find out I ran right past the patient. I let her out the
door and told her to elope and then I ran out behind her
and she didn't do anything but duck behind the bushes and
watch me run. That's just how I missed her. She just stood
right there and watched me run after her. So you will have
situations like this.

You will run into them but also I forgot to mention the
fact that when a patient has been in the hospital eleven
or fifteen years they get so scared of the outside that sometimes you almost have to push them all the way out. One
patient of mine hadn't been off the hospital grounds for
eleven years and I felt that she was at the level to go but
she was just scared. So it was my bright idea, I told her
I wanted her to go down town and I wanted her to go to
Woolworth's and I wanted her to buy a handkerchief and
I wanted her to bring it back to me. And the only way
I was to know that she went to Woolworth's was that I
wanted her to bring me back the sales slip that said Woolworth's on it. So I unlocked the door and I told her she
could go. She stood right outside the door and didn't move.
So I went outside the door, marched her down the steps,
marched her around all the buildings, put her on the bus,
and then stepped back off the bus. Then I held my breath.
I went back to the ward and said, "CNO is going to call
me pretty soon and ask me if I have lost my mind, because
the police are going to have her down there somewhere."
But she went to Woolworths and she came back with the
sales slip and she brought me the handkerchief. And after
that she eloped. So, she learned how to go to town—she
went clear to Kansas City. They called me up and said,

"Mrs. Wash, is this your patient?" I said, "Yes mam."
She said, "Well, I will tell you what, you will have to get
in a State car and go to Kansas City and get her out of
jail," because that is where she was at. I was awfully angry.
I got in the State car, I went all the way to Kansas City
and when I got up there—of course, they didn't know
anything about the project in Kansas City—and out she
walked out of the jail, when they let her out of the cell—
"Oh hi, Mrs. Wash, how are you?" And I looked at her and
said, "Don't you dare grin at me." And the jail keeper
looked at me as if to say, "My gosh, this aide talking to
this patient like that!" I said, "If you were going to elope
you should have stayed gone and got you a job and then I
wouldn't have had to come after you. That is the only way
you do that."

But, anyway, I enjoyed working on the project. A lot of
times we cried, a lot of times we pulled out our hair, a
lot of times we wanted to quit because some of the other
aides we had trouble with, nursing service gave us quite
a bit of trouble, especially me. But it was always rewarding
when a patient would get to the level that we could dis-
miss them. That was the only reward we had because we
didn't get any more pay for this, you understand. They
didn't give us a pay raise for working on this project. We
got paid just like the rest of the aides. We just worked
harder, that's all. But we were rewarded with the patient
getting well and getting back out of the hospital, and
seeing them on the street somewhere and knowing that they
were doing just fine.

Also I have seen a couple of my patients since the project.
I started to LPN (Licensed Practical Nurse) school in
October. I quit the hospital for a couple of months when
school first started and, of course, when one of my patients
heard that I had quit the hospital, that I had resigned, she
came out there especially to bring me a necklace and
earring set. This is the very patient that caught me in a
corner one time and knocked me up side the head and made
me see stars. She didn't like me too well at first but
evidently after I let her out of the hospital she got to
liking me. She came back to visit me. She still holds her
job. She works at a drug store. She has held her job for
four years now. So that is rewarding. You don't give up. If
you get in hot water, you just keep going, because you will
have failures and you are going to get disgusted and everything, but the most rewarding thing is when you see a
patient get well. Then you know that you have done a job
and it is well done.

9

Outcome

The researchers began the Ward H project with certain specified principles and goals but little else. There was little prior knowledge or awareness of what might be the most fruitful variables to investigate. The goals of the project were quite general and did not at the time of its initiation lend themselves to specific delineation. Rather than predetermining a structure and hypotheses to be tested, the project staff chose to clarify for itself its basic principles and assumptions, apply these consistently throughout its course, and let the situation take them where it might.

The most important methodological concern was consistency in the application of the agreed-upon principles. Internal consistency was the hallmark whereby the integrity of the project was preserved. But even as it was felt that an internally consistent system had been achieved, some method of empirical evaluation had to be developed wherever possible to pull the researchers outside the system to take a better look at it. It is difficult to evaluate innovative projects such as the Ward H study. Such projects are undertaken under conditions where there is insufficient information for setting up a research design: the pertinent variables are unknown; control populations are not always available, and the study must be conducted in a clinical setting with little separation from practical service needs. In the current study, for example, it would not have been feasible to set up a matched control group of patients. Ward H was the one remaining "back ward" of the hospital. The Ward H patients themselves were specifically selected as unique in their intractability to other forms of treatment. So, rather than the traditional control group, an "own-control" technique was used, i.e., the patients were evaluated early in the project and by this means established their own baseline from which all future evaluations could be judged.

Innovative studies must be adaptable and flexible so that much about the methodology, technique and approach may be altered before the study is complete. For this reason, too, the assessment of such studies in an extremely rigorous, traditional manner is impossible. But, despite these difficulties, innovative projects must be subjected to thoughtful and careful evaluation wherever possible.

With the above limitations in mind, two different goals were set for data collection. The first of these was to follow the process of the evolvement of the project. The effort here was to delineate the problems with which the project had to cope and the attempted solutions to these problems. A description of this process has been the task of the preceding chapters of this book. The second goal was to differentiate critical variables and then devise a means of measuring them. The major tool of data collection was that of naturalistic observation. As trends and concepts began to emerge, these were established as significant variables. Once measured, efforts were made to relate them to other variables and this became a continuing process. Each variable pointed to others so that the process of generating them and attempting to measure them continued until the termination of the project.

During its course many variables that had been considered as significant turned out not to be so. With others, the efforts at measurement proved to be inconclusive. For example, a Behavioral Inventory Scale was developed during the second year of the project and was to be utilized by the aides in rating patient progress. The scale, while having a useful heuristic and feedback effect for the aides, proved to be extremely unreliable and therefore not adequate in demonstrating the impact of the project on the patient population in a scientific sense.

Initially it was believed that the project could have impact in four areas: the patients; the aides; the project professional staff, and its host institution, Topeka State Hospital. It appeared that some of the more traditional techniques might be relevant to measuring these areas; therefore, they were applied early in the project. For example, commonly used psychological tests were administered and a project log was established. Other techniques were devised later when their need became apparent, e.g., the Behavioral Inventory Scale and the Aide-Patient Relationship Q-Sort. Some areas of observation never did lend themselves to measurement. At best the project was able only to attempt a systematic conceptualization of these areas of observation with the expectation that in time the pertinent variables would become more clear and more finely elaborated.

In this chapter, then, both "hard" and inferential or speculative data will be presented. The "hard" data represent those instances in which the researchers were able to both specify and measure pertinent variables. The more inferential data represent less complete working-through of the data collection process.

EFFECT ON PATIENTS

In evaluating the effect upon the patients three classes of data were available to the investigators: the observation of ward behaviors; data pertaining to discharge and readmission rate that permitted a comparison with other patient populations in the hospital, and data that was concerned with the outcome of specific predictions made about the patients early in the project.

Observable Ward Behaviors

This class of inferences pertains to the "normalization" of the patient in his milieu, that is, the degree to which the patient began to behave more like the usual conception of a normal human being or the extent to which the patients came within the range of conventional acceptable behavior and were able to impress others with their normalcy.

Inferences concerning the normalcy of the patient were drawn from comparisons made at various points in time from the project log, from photographs of the ward, and from a frequency count kept of specified critical incidents or events in the life of the patient (Table 1). These critical incidents generally are used by the staff of the institution as gross indications of change in the condition of patients. For comparison purposes, the frequency of the occurrence of these incidents is presented for a three month period early in the project and a comparable period in the last year of the project.

TABLE 1

Frequency of Critical Incidents on Ward H
Pre- and Post-Project Comparisons

Incidents on Ward	Frequency	
	9/60 to 12/60	2/64 to 5/64
Off-ground Passes	74	233
Escapes	7	3
Number of Patients on Jobs and Industrial Assignments	2	17
Visits by Relatives	42	15
Assaults	39	4

In addition to the quantitative indications of improvement certain observable phenomena can be described. First among them was the improved physical appearance of the patients. By the end of the project most of the Ward H patients were able to dress neatly and appropriately for their age, role, and the activity in which they were participating. They used cosmetics more appropriately. There was a marked lessening of bizarreness in their facial gestures, bodily postures and gait. In fact, when some of the non-project hospital staff were conducted on a tour of the ward, many of them did not realize that their guides were patients.

Secondly, there was marked normalization of the environment in which the patient lived. At the inception of the project one would have noted immediately the extent to which the living environment of Ward H was concerned with the restraint and protection of the patients. As is evident in photographs taken on the ward early in the project, the doors were locked; the radiators had covers; the televison was encased; the ward was remarkably barren. There had been a systematic effort to remove everything that the patients might use to hurt themselves or others. By the end of the project there was far less concern with restraint and with fears of patients doing injury to themselves or others. Quite frequently the door to the ward was left unlocked. Everywhere there was decorative bric-a-brac which formerly would have been considered dangerous but which now reflected events or interpersonal transactions in the lives of the patients. The ward had a personal, homey quality and had lost much of its institutional appearance.

Another dimension of this movement towards normalcy was the more modulated quality of the patients' actions and language. There was much less crazy talk, and openly delusional or autistic patients had become a rarity. As is indicated in Table 1, the frequency of assault and escape had decreased markedly. Eating habits had improved. One seldom saw patients with bizarre mannerisms. There was a marked decrease in generalized explosive hostility across the ward.

Another dimension was that of sociability. There were now fewer isolates on the ward. Patients talked more to each other. There was a sense of group cohesiveness about them. They attended hospital social functions, participated in group planning and group projects and seemed more capable of appropriate heterosexual behavior.

And, finally, by the end of the project the patients manifested most of the competencies and skills which we find in normals. They were able to sew, to make use of table manners; they could use and budget money and make their way downtown on the city transportation system. More of them were able to work either downtown or in the hospital on an industrial assignment (Table 1). They were capable of adequate personal care and hygiene; they were able to make visits to their relatives. Consistent with this, the incident data in Table 1 show an increase in the number of off-ground passes and a decrease in the number of visits by relatives. Since patients were now going home on passes more frequently, relatives visited the hospital less often. Most patients were also able to perform their share of the housekeeping tasks on the ward. To an outside observer the kinds of changes that had occurred over the four years of the project were indeed dramatic.

Comparative Data

The second major class of data collected by the project was concerned with discharge and readmission rates and personnel costs. Comparisons were drawn between the Ward H patients and the remainder of the chronic population at Topeka State Hospital that was in the same statistical cohort. This group could not be considered a formal control group but as individuals who carried the same diagnostic label as those on Ward H. Taken collectively, they were more similar to the Ward H population than any other group in the hospital. They were different as they required less restraint and control.

TABLE 2

Discharge Rate Comparisons between Ward H and the Adult Chronic Population at TSH from the Same Cohort* for the Period June 1960–June 1964

	Total Population	Number Discharged **	Discharge Rate
H	36	19	53%
TSH Females (excluding H)	213	106	50%
TSH Males	228	124	54%
Total TSH (excluding H)	441	230	52%

* The cohort under consideration is that hospitalized prior to July 1, 1959 with the diagnosis of chronic schizophrenia.

** Patients discharged after July 1960, but readmitted before June 1964 were not tabulated as discharged.

As has been indicated by the observational data, there had been substantial improvements in the direction of normalcy on the part of the patients. The statistics concerning the discharge rate were consistent with this observation. Over the life of the project the discharge rate on Ward H was at least equivalent to that for all other chronic schizophrenic patients at Topeka State Hospital in the same statistical cohort despite the fact that the Ward H patients were presumably the more intractable patients.

Positive improvement was observed in all patients on Ward H but was less noticeable in the older and more chronic of its patients. The project had its most profound effect on younger patients and on those patients who had been hospitalized for shorter periods of time (Table 3).

TABLE 3

Comparative Discharge Rates
in Relation to Years of Hospitalization

Years in Hospital	Ward H	TSH Adult Chronic Population		
		Female	Male	Total
1–5	80%	61%	50%	57%
5–15	40%	43%	36%	45%
15–25	20%	24%	43%	36%
25+	33%	31%	50%	42%

As with other projects, the Ward H study found the effects of long term institutionalization most difficult to combat. In terms of the discharge rate, the Ward H program was more effective than the regular hospital program for those patients who had been hospitalized for five years or less. The discharge rate on Ward H for this group of patients was 80%. For other female chronic schizophrenics in the hospital the rate was 61%.

During the last year of the project, that is, from June 1963 to June 1964, forty-five of the 247 patients that remained out of the original cohort were discharged. While Ward H conained only 15% of this population, it accounted for 25% of the discharges against 17% for the remainder of the hospital (Table 4).

TABLE 4

Comparative Discharge Rates June 1963–June 1964
for Chronic Cohort

	Total Population	Number Discharged	Discharge Rate
H	36	9	25%
TSH (excluding H)	211	36	17%
Total TSH	247	45	18%

In terms of readmission data, of the nineteen patients discharged from the original cohort on Ward H only one patient (5.3%) had been readmitted to the hospital by December of 1965. The average length of stay out of the hospital for the dichargees was 23 months with a range from 15 to 49 months. Comparable data was available for the non-Ward H patients that were discharged from this cohort. Topeka State Hospital statistics indicate that the readmission rate was 36.9% (Table 5).

To compare the economy of the Ward H program with other continued closed-ward treatment programs for chronic schizophrenics in Topeka State Hospital, efforts were made to determine costs per patient. Since the cost

TABLE 5

Ward H Readmission Data

	Ward H	TSH* (excluding H)
Patients Discharged	19	311
Patients Readmitted (as of December 1965)	1	115
Readmission Rate	5.3%	36.9%

*Adult chronic schizophrenic population at Topeka State Hospital in the same cohort from which the Ward H patients were drawn.

of housing and maintenance were equivalent, only personnel costs were computed and these were based on the daily wage rate of the ward's clinical staff. Research personnel who served no clinical function were excluded from the Ward H figure. Clinical personnel costs were computed for seven other continued treatment wards; the costs for the least and the most expensive wards are presented in Table 6. The cost of personnel time on Ward

TABLE 6

Comparison of Personnel Costs Ward H and Other TSH Closed Continued Treatment Wards

Personnel Costs	H	Comparison Ward Range	
		Low	High
Dollars per patient per day	$2.60	$2.60	$3.00
Percentage of personnel costs allocated to aide salaries	79%	50%	43%

H was equivalent to that of the least expensive continued treatment ward. Since these wards are generally the least expensive of any in a hospital, the clinical program on Ward H was one of the most economical in the entire hospital. In addition, a larger proportion of the personnel costs on Ward H was allocated to aide salaries than was allocated to professional staff salaries, a fact especially relevant in view of the critical shortage of professional manpower in state mental hospitals and the greater availability of psychiatric aides.

In summary, then, the comparative data appear to confirm the observational data on the Ward H patients. Ward H, as a whole, had a discharge rate equivalent to that of the whole hospital for chronic schizophrenic patients from the same cohort. For patients who were institutionalized less than five years, this rate was somewhat higher than that for the rest of the hospital, and the readmission rate to date has been dramatically lower. These results were especially remarkable in view of the fact that the Ward H population was generally assumed to be the least amenable to treatment. At the same time, the personnel cost of the Ward H program was equivalent to that of the least expensive ward in the hospital.

Predictive Data

On the basis of the principles, the theory, and the process of development of the Ward H project, certain predictions were possible. Three types of predictions were made: those pertaining to outcome of treatment for patients; those pertaining to rate of improvement, and those pertaining to kind or quality of improvement in patient functioning.

At the inception of the project, once the patient population had been selected, the ward staff established three treatment goals for patients: for some patients the expected outcome of treatment was that of discharge to independent living; for a second category an improved adjustment in the hospital; for the remainder discharge to a supervised living situation, i.e., a nursing home placement.

The initial judgments for placing the patients in each of these predictive categories were made by the ward staff, i.e., the aides, the ward physician, the nurse and social worker. Each patient was discussed until a consensus was arrived at. The criteria used in arriving at these judgments were the apparent capacity of the patient to enter into meaningful contact with the aide staff and the availability of family resources that could be used in the rehabilitation of the patient. Each of these predictive categories contained twelve patients.

For the first category the goal of discharge to independent living was achieved for 11 of the 12 patients. For the twelfth patient, although behavioral improvement had been achieved, the patient's family situation proved to be inordinately complex and the patient remained undischarged at the termination of the project.

For the group of patients for whom improved adjustment in the hospital was predicted the goals appear to have been exceeded. While only slight improvement was seen in two of the patients, three of this group were eventually discharged. Of the three, one was discharged to a nursing home and two to their families. Of the two

TABLE 7

Outcome of Predicted Treatment

Goals	Number of Patients	Results			
		Still in Hospital		Discharged or Paroled	
		Slight Improvement	Moderate Improvement	Substantial Improvement	Discharged
1. Discharged to independent living	12	1		11	
2. Improved adjustment in hospital	12	2	4	3	3
3. Discharged to nursing home	12	Insufficiently improved for nursing home placement — 1	Could be placed when nursing home available — 6	Placed — 5	

discharged to their families, one was readmitted to the hospital after the project was terminated.

Of those patients for whom the goal was discharge to a nursing home, eleven had improved sufficiently for placement by the end of the project. However, of the eleven, only five had been placed. For Ward H patients as for those in the rest of the hospital, only a limited number of nursing home vacancies was available, and it was usually necessary for patients to wait for these vacancies to occur even though their adjustment was adequate.

In summary, with the exception of two patients, treatment goals were achieved or exceeded.

The second type of prediction was concerned with the rate of improvement. It was expected that it would take a period of time for the aides to relate usefully and therapeutically to the patients, and that it would take further time for the relationship to have a significant impact on the patients. It was anticipated that with Ward H, as with other projects, there would be a rapid improvement initially in response to a project being put into effect and to concomitant alterations in the environment. Once this period was over, however, it was felt that it would take approximately two years before any further substantial improvements were noted. As can be seen in Table 8, this proved to be the case. The discharge rate was ex-

TABLE 8

Annual Discharge Rate*

Year	Number Discharged	Discharge Rate
1960–61	2	6%
1961–62	1	3%
1962–63	7	19%
1963–64	17	46%

* Includes patients from the same cohort transferred to Ward H to fill vacancies created by discharges among the original 36 patients.

tremely low during the first two years of the project and then accelerated during the third year. During the final year the discharge rate was 46% for the ward. This finding gave credence to one of the basic assumptions of the project, that is, that improvement and growth in chronic schizophrenic patients requires an enduring relationship.

The final set of predictive data had to do with quality and kinds of changes that would take place in patients. The data available here, again, was in the form of observations of the ward and clinical staff, notations in the project log, and psychological test material.

As previously mentioned, it was decided soon after the project got under way that all patients included in the study would be given periodically a battery of psychological tests. The core battery selected included the Object Assembly subtest from the Wechsler-Bellevue Intelligence Scale, the BRL Object Sorting Test and three figure drawings. The plan was to repeat the battery every three months, but this proved impractical. In actual practice an interval of eight to nine months occurred between test administrations, and almost all of the patients were tested three times. In addition to the core battery, all patients were given the Rorschach test twice: once as soon as possible following the first administration of the core battery, and a second time at discharge or at the end of the project, whichever came first.

It was agreed that a battery likely to be sensitive to changes in psychological functioning of chronic schizophrenic patients should be used. Tests were selected through clinical experience in sequential testing of schizophrenic patients.

For example, it had been noted that some of the subtests of the Wechsler-Bellevue Intelligence Scale seem more sensitive to changes in the schizophrenic patients' functioning than others. More specifically, it appeared that as a schizophrenic patient became more organized and goal-directed, some of the subtest scores went up. One of the performance subtests which had frequently reflected this type of improvement was the Object Assembly. Since an improvement in organization and goal-directedness of patients on Ward H was to be logically predicted on the basis of the theory, this subtest was then selected for inclusion in the test battery. And, since improved ego organization with its accompanying improvement in concept formation and abstract thinking was also predicted on the basis of the theory, the BRL Object Sorting Test was also included.

Figure drawings were included in the test battery because they tend to reveal the patient's experience of himself, that is, his awareness of his own body and identity. Again, improvements in self-awareness and in the development of self-identity were predicted from the theory and the treatment technique. The patient was asked to

TABLE 9

Summary of t-Tests on Trend Analysis
of Psychological Test Data on Patients

Test Variable	Code #	Mean	St. Error	t = value	N	P
Obj. Assem.	1	4.000	1.131	3.537	32	.01
BRL Act.	2	13.791	3.916	3.521	32	.01
BRL Pass.	3	11.697	3.463	3.377	32	.01
Goodenough	4	2.719	1.668	1.630	32	NS
DAP Fig. 1 Pl.	5	.500	.272	1.836	32	NS
DAP Fig. 1 Size	6	.156	.287	.544	32	NS
DAP Fig. 1 M	7	.188	.202	.929	32	NS
DAP Fig. 1 Detail	8	.438	.214	2.045	32	.05
DAP Fig. 1 Qual.	9	.328	.179	1.832	32	NS
DAP Fig. 1 Rel. Adeq.	10	.406	.176	2.308	32	.05
DAP Fig. 1 Lines	11	−.063	.193	−.324	32	NS
DAP Fig. 2 Pl.	12	.734	.340	2.156	32	.05
DAP Fig. 2 Size	13	.703	.332	2.117	32	.05
DAP Fig. 2 M	14	.234	.184	1.275	32	NS
DAP Fig. 2 Detail	15	.453	.190	2.389	32	.05
DAP Fig. 2 Qual.	16	.469	.157	2.954	32	.01
DAP Fig. 2 Rel. Adeq.	17	.250	.177	1.414	32	NS
DAP Fig. 2 Lines	18	.078	.201	.388	32	NS
DAP Fig. 3 Pl.	19	.922	.329	2.806	32	.01
DAP Fig. 3 Size	20	.938	.342	2.743	32	.01
DAP Fig. 3 M	21	.609	.202	3.020	32	.01
DAP Fig. 3 Detail	22	.813	.239	3.393	32	.01
DAP Fig. 3 Qual.	23	.781	.163	4.782	32	.01
DAP Fig. 3 Rel. Adeq.	24	.797	.190	4.187	32	.01
DAP Fig. 3 Lines	25	.328	.203	1.617	32	NS

df = 31 α = .05   t ≥ 2.04

make three drawings: a same sex, an opposite sex, and a self drawing.

A quantitative scoring system was devised for both the BRL Object Sorting Test and the drawings.[1] Since all three tests (the Object Assembly, the BRL, and the drawings) were quantified, the data derived from them could be subjected to statistical analysis. The results of this analysis are to be found in Table 9. Inspection of Table 9 indicates that significant changes were obtained on the Object Assembly, the BRL Object Sorting Test, and the self drawing. Less impressive results were obtained from the drawings of the same and opposite sexes. The results are interpreted as indicating significant improvement in goal-directedness, in cognitive organizational ability, in concept formation and in self-awareness. The results are consistent with predicted improvement.

A clinicial comparison of the pre- and post-testing on the Rorschach was made to obtain insight into the quality of internal changes that might have accrued in the patients rather than as an index of change itself. The inferences drawn from these data must be considered as clinical and, consequently, more speculative than the data previously presented.

An essential aspect of DesLauriers theory is that schizophrenia arises out of a disturbance of body image and self-awareness. In view of the theory, then, it would be expected that improvement in these two areas would be observed. This appeared to be confirmed by the significant changes obtained on self drawing. Much of the material gained from the Rorschach test also appeared to be consistent with this finding. In general, the patient had become capable of an increasingly relevant and meaningful experience of "me" at a physical, psychological and social level. This "me-ness" was indicated by an increased capacity for the experience of one's self as a total being, in interaction with the environment. An example of increased self-experience in a regressed patient was her response to the aide's off-time days. Experiencing a sense of loss, she would say to the aide upon her return that she had missed her. A more intact patient demonstrated her increased

[1] Detailed description of this scoring system can be found in Appendix B.

self-experience by a more meaningful capacity to see herself as a woman, a sexual person, and as someone with a specific social role.

Thought disorder has long been noted as one of the more prominent symptoms of schizophrenia. The concrete, autistic and illogical nature of the schizophrenic's thought processes have been well-documented. If improvement were to take place in the schizophrenic, one would expect that his capability for abstract thinking or for more adequate concept formation would improve. The significant changes obtained on the BRL Object Sorting Test confirm the fact that this improvement did occur with the patients on Ward H. The patients were generally more able to symbolize and verbalize their experiences and could deal with them more abstractly. They were now able to get more distance and perspective on themselves and the world and to gain meaning from their experiences. The example was given earlier of the young teenage patient who was able to deal in a more realistic way with the experience of dating. She was able to articulate previously undifferentiated feelings as sexual feelings. She was able to form concepts about them, symbolize with words, and in this way draw on her own previous experience and that of her aide. The pre- and post-Rorschachs also confirmed that improvement in symbolizing and verbalizing had taken place. There were many protocols with a much better and clearer elaboration of percepts (an increased F+ percentage).

As the project went on, other variables relating to the kinds of changes that could be expected in patients became apparent. Because they evolved later on in the project, however, they were not adequately measured or tested. Among these were:

(1) The capacity for increased control; not only the capacity for restraint and delay of impulse but also for increased capacity to modulate one's self, to mesh one's self with the environment. Affect and thinking came to display a more differentiated and complex quality. The patient's response to herself and to the world had less the quality of an all-or-none global reaction. Rather, the response was more specific, more influenced by the subtleties and nuances of human interaction. For the most

regressed patient, this change might be demonstrated on the Rorschach test, e.g., on the first test the patient looked at a particular blot and said, "This is a smudged liver." Later on she was able to say, "This looks like the picture of a smudged liver." A more intact patient demonstrated the same new skills. Early in the project she insisted on discussing as possible jobs those with high status for which she had no skills. Later on the same patient could evaluate with her aide a babysitting job and say that she was much too perfectionistic and liked things to be too well-scheduled and ordered to take a job where she had to care for young infants.

(2) Increased capacity for obtaining gratification and support from human interaction. Early in the project many patients had been social isolates and, when disturbed, had tried to overcome their overwhelming feelings of anxiety and stress by becoming delusional, by hallucinating, or by lying on the floor. As the project continued, they were able to turn increasingly to their aides and eventually to their fellow patients, their families, and their friends and employers for help at times of stress. Not only did they turn to people for support, but they had developed an improved ability to get gratification from them. It was impressive to see, over the course of the project, how patients became close friends, looked forward to doing things together, shared experiences, and appreciated one another. It was considered that it was the intensive relationship with another human being, that is, the aide, that was the major factor in bringing about this kind of change.

(3) Increased internal growth. As the patient was able to grow and develop inner resources, she was able to function in a more autonomous fashion. It became evident that many of the patients had proceeded through a series of developmental growth phases analogous to those seen in children. The increased maturation accompanying these developmental sequences was reflected in a new inner freedom, flexibility and resiliency. The patient became an autonomous and separate individual able to assume a differentiated role in her social group. In many of the pre- and post-Rorschachs it was evident that what had happened was not simply a sealing over of the pa-

thology as is typical with reconstituted chronic schizophrenic patients, but an actual development of internal resources. The number of healthy responses on the Rorschach test increased. The bizarre responses tended to lose some of their immediacy and were placed in greater perspective. Movement responses became much more elaborated and realistic.

The results of the Ward H project appear to be most impressive in this area of growth of the patient's internal resources. Behavioral improvement without evidence of development internally is generally fragile at best. When support is given to most chronic patients, they are able to manage a brittle reconstitution which soon dissipates in the face of stress or the withdrawal of the support. What seemed to occur in the patients on Ward H was an internal change which had increased their capacity for autonomy. The project directors' conclusion was that these changes came about primarily because of a sustained, consistent relationship of the patient to a devoted, spontaneous, intrusive aide. The aide acted spontaneously and in her own personal style of functioning, but in a way consistent with the general principles of the theory that had been formulated with her.

In summary, then, among the more dramatic results of the project were the following:

—The patients developed an improved capacity to conduct themselves in socially acceptable ways;
—For most patients there is evidence that this improvement was accompanied by a proliferation of internal resources that helped the patients to become more independent;
—In personnel costs the program was among the least expensive in the hospital for chronic patients;
—The number of discharges from this ward was at least equivalent to the number discharged from other chronic wards, but the early evidence is that readmission rates are significantly lower.

EFFECT ON AIDES

As described in earlier chapters, changes occurred not only in the patients but also in the aides who cared for them. The project staff, using anecdotal and observational methods, described the change in the aides over the four years of the project as increased involvement, spontaneity, autonomy and initiative (see Chapters 4 through 8). These observations were corroborated by psychological test data obtained on the aides during the course of the project.

In discussions early in the project it was hypothesized that changes in the aides would take the form of an alteration in their need systems. To see if this were so, it was decided to administer the Edwards Personal Preference Schedule to the aides early in the course of the project and again at its termination. For most of the aides there was a three-year interval between testings. The concern of the project directors was alterations in the need system of the aides as a function of their having fulfilled a specific role in a particular kind of administrative organization. Therefore, it was felt that it would be most appropriate to evaluate changes not in terms of their clinical merit but in terms of vocational considerations. The tests, then, were submitted to an industrial psychologist who had broad and extensive experience with the Edwards Test in vocational situations. In his initial instructions the industrial psychologist was told that all the subjects were female psychiatric aides between 30 and 50 years of age. The tests, both pre- and post-, were identified as such and the time interval between them was indicated. He was provided with the following list of questions to guide him in his analysis:

(1) What changes took place in each of the aides? [2]

(2) Describe the characteristics of the group of aides on the pre-test.

> The pre-group had a number of interesting characteristics. The achievement motive appeared to be somewhat muted. It never went beyond the 60th percentile, indicating that the need for getting ahead and being successful was not

[2] The actual pre- and post-profiles for each aide and the summary of changes undergone by each aide can be found in Appendix C. In general, substantial changes were found in six of the eight aides.

very strongly felt or expressed. It was also interesting that the group showed a definite trend toward being deferent. This group appeared to be very tradition-, precedent-, and standard-bound. There was a definite tendency towards conventionality and conformity, and towards immediately responding to external pressures. The pre-group as a group showed only average to above average need for autonomy. Approximately 75% of this group was either average or below average in the autonomy need. Combining the relatively high deference with low autonomy, we have a group of individuals who tend to be overly deferent and on the dependent side. Another important aspect of the pre-group was the generally low affiliation score. The affiliation score was below average for about 85% of this group. This suggests that basically this group was not very gregarious or group-oriented; there appears to be a definite aloofness. This group is also characterized by the fact that as a whole it is not very sensitive to the feelings and motives of others. Dominance also tends to be a bit on the low side in this group. Approximately 75% of this group was average to below average for this need. This goes along with the somewhat low autonomy and the high deference. It suggests that this group as a whole was not very comfortable in assuming a supervisory role. They appear to have trouble initiating, advising, leading, and directing. Much more attention was given to conformity, tradition, and detail than was given to supervising others or influencing the thoughts and activities of other people. Another interesting aspect of this group was the tendency for nurturance to be on the low side. The entire group was either average to below average on this need. This suggests that the group as a whole experienced some difficulty in being sympathetic, forgiving, and affectionate towards others. The group also tended to be low on the endurance scale. Approximately 85% of this group was either average or below average on this scale, suggesting that persistence was somewhat on the weak side. It is also significant that the heterosexual scale for the entire group was on the high side. 75% of this group was above average on this scale. In addition, one of the most striking findings was the high aggression score. Over 85% of this group was above average on this scale, indicating that this group has a strong need to make fun of others, to blame others when things go wrong, and to be somewhat argumentative.

In summary, this group appeared to be relatively low achievers who were overly deferent, conventional, and tradition-bound, and who tended to adjust to their environment in a somewhat dependent fashion. Affiliation and nurturant needs are also on the low side, suggesting that the group tends to be somewhat reticent and aloof in interpersonal situations. The high aggression score suggests that this group harbors resentment and anger. However, in all probability, it is moderated or neutralized due to the relatively low dominance and high deference needs. Thus, the aggression does not come out in a candid, authentic fashion. It is probably expressed in much more subtle, passive fashions. The relatively low endurance and achievement scores suggest that this group probably is on the low side in terms of persistence. Work habits are probably not too well organized. Furthermore, the group appears to be rather insensitive to the feelings and motives of others.

(3) Describe the group on the basis of the post-test.

There are several very significant features regarding the post-group. First of all, the achievement motive in the post-group is average to above the average. This indicates that the group has a relatively strong need to achieve, to get ahead, and to accomplish tasks requiring skill and effort, and to have positions which give them prestige and status. There also appears to be a relatively low need for deference in this group. 65% of this group was below average on the deference scale, suggesting that the group tended to be uncomfortable with traditions, norms, and precedents, and has a relatively strong need to do things for themselves and to be independent. They don't particularly like to accept the leadership of others, or to conform to custom and tradition. Another very interesting feature of this group is almost a complete lack of a need for order. 75% of the group was below the average for this need, suggesting that it had little concern for minor details and routine, repetitive tasks. Another interesting aspect of this group is the fact that 75% of the group expressed an above average need for autonomy. This indicates that it has strong needs to function independently, to be able to come and go as it desires, to say what they think, and to be independent of others in making decisions. As with the pre-group, this group also had relatively low affiliation scores. There was a definite rejection of the need to be loyal to friends, to participate in friendly groups, to form new friendships, and to do things with friends rather than alone. However, this group did seem to be quite intraceptive and sensitive to others. Approximately 85% of this group was average to above the average on the intraception scale. This group also appeared to have a very strong need for dominance and for assuming a supervisory role. Thus, low deference, high autonomy, and high dominance were important characteristics of this particular group. This indicates that this group placed a very high premium on directing, initiating, advising, and coordinating. As with the pre-group, this group also had a relatively low need for nurturance and a high need for change, and relatively low needs for endurance. Furthermore, the group had strong heterosexual needs, probably slightly stronger than the pre-group. As with the pre-group, this group was also extremely aggressive. The fact that autonomy and dominance were high, and deference was low, indicates that resentment and anger were probably expressed in a more candid, above-board, authentic fashion.

(4) Describe the characteristic changes that took place in the aides as a group from pre- to post-testing.

There are several significant changes which appear to have occurred between the time that the pre- and post-testing was conducted. First of all, the post-group appears to have a relatively higher drive level or achievement motive. There is a definite tendency on the part of the post-group to want to get ahead, to be successful, and to accomplish tasks requiring skill and effort. Success and achievement appear to have much more meaning to this group. In addition, deference is generally lower in this group, with autonomy and dominance being higher. This suggests that the group has shifted towards questioning past precedents, traditions, norms, and standards. There appears to be a definite break with old conventions. The group appears to be leaning towards doing things which may in the past have been considered to be unconventional or different. The group also appears to have a much stronger need for independence, freedom, and a position which gives them more prestige, control, respect and status. There also appears to be much more comfort and ease with which this group assumes a supervisory role. The pre-group was characterized by the fact that it was very uncomfortable and tense in this type of situation. The post-group appeared to be much more comfortable. Not only is it comfortable in assuming a supervisory role, but the post-group appears to enjoy and derive a great deal of satisfaction out of this role. In general, the post-group appears to be much less dependent, yielding, conforming and submissive, and far more independent and autonomous. Furthermore, the sensitivity of the group towards other people appears to be increased, although the post-group still has low affiliation and nurturant needs. In relating to people, there appears to be a definite loosening up. The post-group appears to be more spontaneous, open, and more informal. It does not appear to be nearly as inhibited as the pre-group. There is also a general drop in the need for order in the post-group. This may reflect a moving away from being overly concerned with minute, routine, mechanical, repetitive details and a stronger concern for the general aspects of their environment. Furthermore, the significant movement in this group is the fact that the level of aggression appears to have gone up. The fact that aggression has gone up with an increased dominance and autonomy and a decreased deference, suggests that aggression is expressed much more openly and candidly. The post-group handles feelings of resentment in a very open fashion, while the pre-group appeared to express it in a subtle, passive, indirect manner. The post-group is definitely more independent and possibly even rebellious. There is a definite maverick flavor to the post-group. It appears to be the type of group who now questions authority and hierarchal arrangements. They are not restrained any longer by the fear that non-conformity or conventionality may lead to punishment or retaliation. If this group has any difficulty, it is probably that their supervisors are concerned over the fact that they let minor, repetitive details slip by, and that they are overly frank and candid in the expression of their feelings. This group no longer assumes an obedient, deferent kind of role. It is the type of group who will now challenge authority.

In the third year of the project a new instrument became available that permitted the measurement of certain aide attitudes toward patients. This instrument made it possible to compare the attitudes of the Ward H aides with those of other Topeka State Hospital aides as well as with those of aides from other institutions. The instrument was the Aide-Patient Relationship Q-Sort which had been devised as a part of a larger study undertaken at Osawattomie State Hospital, Osawattomie, Kansas. The aide was to sort a series of statements that were self-descriptive of interactions with patients. The character of these interactions was such that they could be arrayed on a dimension corresponding to the "organization centered" versus "patient centered" continuum postulated for hospital social systems. The terms most appropriate for describing this continuum of aide behaviors are "custodial" versus "therapeutic." Within an "organization centered" system the types of aide-patient interaction congruent with that system would stress custodialism in the multiple sense of protection, care, surveillance and guardianship. Within a "patient centered" system the most appropriate aide behaviors would reflect some therapeutic intent based on interpersonal premises. The more appropriate a particular behavior or Q-Sort item might be within one system, the less appropriate it would be within the opposing system. The results obtained from this Q-Sort are indicated in the following report.[3]

The following table (Table 10) shows the mean self-scores for the experimental aide group (Ward H) in comparison to three other groups on the Aide-Patient Relationship Q-Sort. All three groups are part of a sample of 150 aides selected from a variety of eight adult psychiatric institutions which were used in the development of the instrument. The institutions include four state hospitals from three mid-western states; a private hospital; the psychiatric units in a university medical center, and two VA installations. $Q_{1\&2}$ refers to the cluster of most theraupeutically oriented aides isolated from a Q-analysis. "Random" is a sample of 50 aides selected from the original 150. "TSH" includes those 20 non-project aides representing Topeka State Hospital in the development of the instrument. Seven of the latter are also included in the "Random" group.

Ward H exceeds all other groups on three scores and is fairly equal to $Q_{1\&2}$ on Factor I. Factor I is suggestive of an Activity role in which the positive pole indicates opening of possibilities for patients, e.g., "Encourage patients to participate in ward programs and other activities," "Get suggestions when planning something for the ward," "Introduce activities on the ward that are as close as possible to normal life outside the hospital." The negative pole is characterized by items restraining or delimiting patient activity, e.g., "Put in restraint patients who show any likelihood of an outburst," "Keep the good patients separated from the more disturbed in order to prevent them too from becoming sicker." All four groups have positive scores and indicate they are all more concerned with "normalcy" and socialization in contrast to pathology and restraint. However, it is quite apparent that both Ward H and $Q_{1\&2}$ obtained considerably higher scores than the other two groups.

[3] By Lawrence Appleby, Ph.D., project director, Social Systems Project, Osawattomie State Hospital. National Institute of Mental Health Project MH-507.

TABLE 10

Mean Scores and Standard Deviations on Self Q-Sort

Groups		Factors			
		I	II′	IV	Total C
Ward H (N 8)	Mean	12.91*	−1.71	3.02	14.71
	S.D.	4.60	2.88	4.30	10.44
Q$_{1\&2}$ (N 22)	Mean	13.43	−2.91	.73	11.25
	S.D.	3.25	3.15	3.78	6.35
Random (N 50)	Mean	8.24	−5.07	−1.07	2.22
	S.D.	7.16	5.46	3.96	11.59
TSH (N 20)	Mean	4.68	−6.25	−1.36	−2.84
	S.D.	5.58	4.36	4.32	9.48

* The more positive the score, the more the positive pole of the factor is exhibited.

Significance Tests of Mean Differences between Ward H Group and Three Control Groups

Factors	TSH	Groups Random	Q$_{1\&2}$
I	p <.005, >.001	p <.10, >.05**	NS
II′	p <.05, >.025	p <.05*	NS
IV	p <.025, >.01	p <.01, >.005	p <.001
C	p <.001	p <.01	NS*

* Variances are heterogeneous. Variation of t test used to evaluate differences between means. See Edwards, *Experimental Design in Psychological Research*, pp. 106, 1960.

** When deviant subject's score from Ward H group was eliminated, the difference between the means of Ward H and Random group was significant p <.05. (Subject's score on Factor I was second lowest of Ward H scores, $X_i = 6.55$)

All other differences of means tested by t. See Edwards, pp 94.

All of values of t are evaluated as one-tailed tests assuming that the mean for Ward H group would be predictably larger.

Probability levels were obtained from Snedecor, *Statistical Methods*, pp 46, 1946 edition.

Factor II is suggestive of a bodily maintenance role in which the positive pole is aimed at fostering patient initiative and showing a personal concern for the patient. The other pole emphasizes a more impersonal orientation toward the patients' needs—a "front-maintaining" position. The former is characterized by such items as, "Let patients make their own decisions as to appointments with the barber, at the beauty shop," etc., and "Refuse to carry out an order which does not appear to be safe or consistent with a patient's needs." The later includes items such as, "Act cheerful before patients at all times even though I do not always feel that way," and "Clean the patient if he soils himself." Though all groups tended to be more oriented toward the less personal aspects of body-maintenance, the Ward H group was far less so than the other three.

Factor IV can be thought of as a role of "protection"; on one pole, the concern being for a personal protection of the patient and the other a concern for protecting the institution. The former, for example, includes items like, "Defend the patient who is criticized unjustly," and "Give patients who prefer not to be clean the freedom to be dirty if it has therapeutic value at the moment." The latter contains such items as, "Keep patients from disturbing doctors and other staff members," and "Make sure patients use proper language." It is clear from the data that Ward H aide group again exceeds the other three groups and is apparently more involved with tasks concerning the feelings of patients than with institutional control.

"Total C," the underlying dimension of the Q-Sort, measures to what extent a person is therapy-centered and conversely, organizationally-centered. This score is obtained by simply summing the three factor scores and subtracting a repeated item on Factor IV. The data clearly reveal that Ward H is more therapeutically-centered than any of the other groups.

Several additional findings occurred though the data is not listed here. One concerns the professional supervisors ("norm-bearers") on the Ward H project. These people $(N = 3)$, as expected, saw the aides as performing quite positive roles on all factors and rated their performance as being very therapeutically-centered. Given the instructions to sort the items "ideally," these people had even higher mean scores, suggesting that they had very high expectations of role performance on the part of the aide and that there was some awareness that the aides were not actually performing to the degree expected. A similar discrepancy occurred between the "self" and "ideal" sorts for the Ward H aide personnel. Their extremely high expectations, however, indicate that they have incorporated, or are at least cognizant of, the norm-bearers' expectations and see their ideal role performance as quite similar to what their supervisors expect.

Another finding, though perhaps not as significant as the

above, indicates that Ward H is not as concerned with performing tasks that have a high quality of "social desirability" as the other groups. The scale of social desirability is built into the instrument and a score is obtained which indicates the degree to which a subject is responding to situations which would make him "look good in the eyes of the others." While norms are not yet available, the distribution of scores on Ward H clearly suggests that this group is not concerned with performing those tasks that are socially desirable, nor do they appear concerned about making themselves "look good."

The psychological test data on the aides appear to confirm the observed behavioral changes in increased spontaneity, involvement, and autonomy. Perhaps the best example of the aides' level of functioning occurred during a full day colloquium on the project that was held for the staff of Topeka State Hospital. The purpose of the colloquium was to describe the results of the project. The staff was divided into small groups with a Ward H aide as a member of each group to answer questions and discuss the operation of the ward. The impact of the aides on the staff was consistently and highly positive. The staff found themselves greatly affected by the aides' degree of security, their sense of confidence, their capacity to articulate, their willingness to discuss what they did know, and their easy acknowledgment of what they did not know—in short, by their maturity, both personal and professional.

EFFECT ON PROJECT PROFESSIONAL PERSONNEL

Not only the hospital staff but also the professional staff on Ward H developed a great respect for the work of the aides. As they worked with these aides, they began to appreciate the results that came from the constructive and effective use of the self. Most of the professional staff, as in any highly educated group, had spent a large portion of their lives in academic settings learning theories and techniques devised by others. They had had little opportunity to experiment and test out the applicability of what they had learned to their own personal styles. The project gave them an opportunity to observe and work closely with a group of aides who had not had academic training and who were not overwhelmed by the value of theoretical and technical learning. The aides had relied instead upon their own personal styles of behavior and living and generally regarded any imposition of technique or theory inconsistent with their personal styles as a violation of their integrity. When presented with theoretical material, the aides would pick and choose freely among techniques, selecting those that would best enable them to make more effective use of themselves. In other words, the aides used theory and technique as a complement to the use of self, not as a substitute for it. For the professional staff, exposure to this point of view had a liberating effect. By allowing themselves to participate in a relationship styled by the aides they also allowed themselves to come to an appreciation of effectiveness as a function of personal style. It was probably this exposure that most strongly motivated the professional staff to cooperate in opening new possibilities for the aides rather than to impose restraints on them. The Ward H professional and aide staff demonstrated a remarkable congruence in their perception and experience of each others' roles. There was a strong consensus between them as to the impact, the power and the value of each member of the project group.

The professional staff's appreciation of the aides was not a superficial gesture to pay lip service to the quality of their work. Their engagement with them had resulted in basic attitudinal changes, changes not only at the level of their conscious estimates of one another, but also at a deep emotional level.

In contrast to the usual role pattern in a hospital hierarchy, in this project it was the professional staff that was expected to be flexible. In most organizations the upper level sets the norms and the least skilled and trained members at the lower level are expected to conform and adapt to them. Logically, however, the professional's education and training prepare him better to be flexible and the burden of adaptability should be easier on him. Thus, on Ward H it was the aides who set the standards and styles for interpersonal relationships and the professional staff who adapted to them.

It was interesting that those who observed the ward professional staff felt that they were inclined to act in behalf of the aides rather than the hospital. Whenever a valid, legitimate conflict of issues arose, the staff's tendency was to expect the hospital to adapt to the needs of the aides. While the aides had demonstrated earlier their inclination to act in behalf of the patient rather than the organization, the staff's new expectation that the hospital should adapt to the aides' requests was more remarkable because their natural bias was to be loyal first to their organization or their profession.

It became evident that the staff had undergone changes in their attitudes about the functions of authority, responsibility and accountability. In the past this group had thought of authority as synonymous with power. With the evolution of the project, the staff was able to acknowledge that all members of the project had power to influence the course of events. Authority came to mean *supporting the subordinate in the use of his power to achieve the project's goals*. In effect, each individual had authority in separate realms. The aide had authority in relation to the patients; the nurse had authority in relation to the aides. That is, by virtue of her authority it was the nurse's function to support the aide in the use of her authority in the treatment of patients. In other words, the authority of the nurse was of a different kind than that of the aide and did not supplant it or diminish it.

Responsibility, too, was defined in new ways. Formerly, each member of the staff had seen himself as responsible for dispensing a particular and limited kind of service. He saw himself as a member of a team in which the members combined had all of the skills necessary for treating a patient. The responsibility was shared, and part of the team responsibility was to draw out the particular and well-defined service each member could offer. The aide served as the eyes and ears of the professional staff only because she was with the patients all of her working hours. In this traditional frame of reference it would have been preferable to the members of the professional staff for themselves to have been with the patients at all times since they could then have had the best possible information on which to base a treatment program and could have carried out the treatment in the most effective way possible. Since this was clearly an impossible goal, the aide was directed to carry out what the staff would like to have done. Under this system the aides were considered to be "helpers" to the professional staff, and their responsibility was to carry out the goals of the staff. On Ward H, however, it was no longer the responsibility of the staff to offer the actual treatment services to the patients. They were responsible instead for developing the personal effectiveness of the aide so that *she* could treat the patient in the best way possible. It was the responsibility of the staff to develop a structure within which effective treatment could take place. Here they were to be of service to the aides in carrying out goals which were defined and agreed upon by the aides rather than, as in the traditional relationship, the aides being of service to them.

Accountability usually means "who is to blame," but with this term, too, the project had a change in emphasis. The focus on Ward H was on the supervisor-supervisee relationship, and accountability was seen as a means of support that the supervisor had available to offer to the supervisee. In supervisory sessions the focus was on the goals of the treatment, and supervision was performed by helping the supervisee to maintain goal-directedness. Once the supervisee had established certain goals as his part of the contract, the supervisor in effect agreed to focus attention upon whether or not results had been achieved. In this process the supervisee was helped to articulate his goals, evaluate results and, if necessary, reevaluate his goals and methods. Accountability was in terms of results rather than the methods whereby results were obtained.

EFFECT ON THE INSTITUTION

It is difficult to assess the effect of the project on the hospital. The ward itself was an isolated unit and although within this unit it was possible to observe, communicate and delineate the variables that seemed to be effective, the relationship of this ward with the hospital was quite different. The project was, of course, only a small part of a larger organization, and it was difficult to tell how the hospital was affected by what was going on there. In any given situation, the project could have been the stimulus that caused changes elsewhere in the hospital. It might have been a catalyst that accelerated ongoing trends or was part of a larger trend, that is, part of a *Zeitgeist*. The project's concurrence with many of these trends was evident. It is difficult to specify to what extent this concurrence was coincidental and to what extent causal.

For example, the hospital began to reappraise the roles of all its personnel and began to look especially at the use it was making of its aides. Although the institution had a history of commitment to the importance of the aide in patient treatment, for many reasons this philosophy had been honored more by the spoken idea than in actual fact. The project demonstrated the validity of the therapeutic capability of the aides. By the time of its completion it was no longer atypical in the institution for an aide to have the responsibility for a group of patients or for her to have an intensive therapeutic relationship on a one-to-one basis.

As training innovations played a key role in carrying out the project, so too had there been important innovations in the institution's inservice training programs. The psychiatric residency program made an important shift. Advanced residents now frequently served as consultants to teams, rather than as ward administrators bearing full responsibility for the therapeutic program. The need for supervisory training for nurses was recognized, and a program to provide it was put into effect.

The institution became increasingly consistent in the application of its philosophy that patient improvement comes about through corrective relationships among human beings rather than through nonpersonal procedures such as electric shock. One of the ways in which the institution implemented this philosophy has been to subdivide treatment units so that they are small enough to permit stable and accessible relationships among staff and patients. Patients are often divided into small groups that will foster stability of relationships among themselves and with the specific staff responsible for them.

Responsibility has been increasingly defined in terms of patients under one's care, rather than in terms of the services one is expected to provide.

On Ward H there had been increased appreciation of the need for compatibility between a treatment program and the administrative structure and practices governing that program. So, too, in the rest of the institution increased focus upon administrative practices was seen as a legitimate and important aspect of the treatment milieu. Within the last year of the project an important reorganization took place in the hospital administration. The purpose of this reorganization was to promote a clearer definition of responsibility among the hospital staff and to place as much of the responsibility as possible in the hands of those immediately concerned with the patients' treatment.

Finally, it was obvious that some alterations had occurred in the hospital's way of approaching problems. Being uncertain about solutions to problems came to have a positive value. Once the uncertainty had been recognized, problems could then be defined and innovative and evaluative efforts could be applied. The hospital became increasingly committed to the need for evaluation of its programs, especially since the goals of those programs, that is, "patient cure," is difficult to define objectively or consensually.

The project terminated September, 1964. It was not possible for the hospital to absorb it as an isolated social system; however, those aspects of the Ward H project that were compatible with the ongoing system were absorbed.

The results of the project, then, may be summarized as follows. Significant and stable improvement was achieved with a formerly intractable group of patients through a program that, shorn of its research aspects, was one of the least expensive in the institution. Through the development of a particular social system, previously unused staff potentials emerged. New approaches to inservice training and staff development were demonstrated. Many of the critical issues of patient treatment and administrative practices were considered.

Aside from freeing more highly trained professionals for

other work and returning a number of people to a functioning role in society who otherwise would have been a burden to it, the most unique aspect of this project was the nature of the relationships among its participants. While the hospital had long had a tradition for humane treatment, the project capitalized upon that which was particularly human. It began by acknowledging people, staff and patients alike, as they were. Its primary aim was to create the conditions through which personal integrity could develop. With integrity came innovation and growth.

10

Overview and Implications

This chapter will summarize the Ward H project: its antecedents, its rationale, and the characteristics of the system that eventually came into being. There will, further, be a discussion of the implications of this work for mental health and for growth-inducing organizations.

ANTECEDENTS AND RATIONALE

The impetus of this project was a growing dissatisfaction with the current treatment of hospitalized chronic schizophrenic patients. There are no doubt many reasons why this treatment process had been ineffective, but only those germane to this project will be mentioned. Although many believe that in order to make significant progress with these patients an enduring relationship is needed, many factors in the treatment institutions preclude the development of this relationship. For example, at the institution where this project was developed, it was routine for the professional staff in training to rotate among the various services of the hospital. The maximum amount of time spent on any particular ward was one year, and because this relatively short time had to be divided among such a large number of patients, it was impossible to establish any kind of long-term relationship.

Not only was professional staff time inadequate for the best treatment of these chronic schizophrenics but there was also a general feeling, implied if not expressed, that staff time and energy could be spent to better purpose. More could be accomplished by working with patients with short-term illness, where the staff could see results from any intervention they might make.

There was a further difficulty. Although there were exceptions, most of the professional staff found it dif-

193

ficult to relate to the chronic patient who generally functioned at a very primitive level. For the professional staff this gap frequently created feelings of self-doubt and pessimism about their ability to produce effective changes among these patients.

The air of pessimism that surrounds the treatment of the chronic schizophrenic patient has resulted, in many instances, in an acceptance of the status quo as the treatment of choice. Whatever progress has been made in the past has rarely been gratifying because even minor changes took long periods of time and were subject to many set-backs. Even the most successful treatments often brought the patient only to a borderline level of functioning.

For these reasons it was apparent to many people at Topeka State Hospital (and in similar organizations) that there was need for a change. Innovations in treatment practices for chronic schizophrenics have been undertaken in many centers in this country and abroad. The Ward H program represents one such effort. The key to innovation in the Ward H program was the specific theoretical approach expounded by Austin DesLauriers. Basic to this theoretical approach was the need for a different kind of relationship between the patient and the person responsible for his treatment—a relationship that emphasized intrusiveness, spontaneity and commitment. The Ward H program *assumed* that these characteristics were within the competence of the psychiatric aides. Since the relationship between the psychiatric aide and the patient was to be the crucial therapeutic modality in this treatment program, the role of the aides had to be altered from the conventional one of helping the professional staff carry out treatment to that of being responsible for carrying out the treatment themselves. The change in the role of the psychiatric aides in turn necessitated an alteration in the role of the professional staff. Previously they had directed treatment, but their new role was to support the aides who carried out the treatment. That is, what had been the professional directing staff now became the professional supporting staff.

CHARACTERISTICS OF THE CULTURE

Such alteration of specific roles was not sufficient to carry out the mandate of this project. Because the individuals who filled these roles functioned interdependently, something far greater than role-change was being developed. In fact, a different culture was being generated. Two major elements characterized this new culture or social system; a specific set of assumptions about people, and a series of principles that related to the problem-solving system.

Assumptions About People

The attitudes toward people that are to be described as characteristic of this culture are not unique to this project. Certainly, many of these attitudes have been recognized. But despite verbal homage to the idea that "people are important," this attitude rarely manifests itself in the day-to-day operations of most organizations.

The orientation of the Ward H project was that the major resource for problem definition and problem-solution was present in its members. This, however, implies certain specific assumptions about the nature of people functioning to complete a task. The first of these is that people want and need to engage in problem-solving efforts; they need to increase their effectiveness and to grow in competency. Since a drive for competency (and with it the growth of one's own self-appraisal and sense of well-being) is so much a part of the philosophy that motivates behavior in western society, this program assumed that people have a drive to increase their effectiveness in problem-solving.

Another characteristic of this culture was that it placed high value on the use of personal style. The effort at growth could best be facilitated when people were accepted as they were, with each one's unique personal style in problem-solving, whatever that might be, recognized as his most effective tool. *Regardless of the individual approach, most people best develop their problem-solving effectiveness within the specific context of a social system*. Whatever the individual approach, the social system must facilitate and encourage its use. The system must be able to tolerate a variety of problem-solving approaches. Given this tolerance, however, the individuality and the personal style of the members of a system potentially become the system's greatest assets.

The key factor in the individual's use of his problem-solving ability is the nature of the relationships that exist among the members of the system. To the extent that the relationships are characterized by spontaneity, autonomy, open and candid communication, and mutual respect, problem solving and growth in individual competence can be facilitated. The task of the system becomes one of supporting and maintaining this style of relationship.

This culture also assumed that the growth in competence which arose from this kind of relationship produced a change in personal identity. Along with such changes, one must expect discomfort and anxiety. Toleration for and effective ways of coping with the discomfort and disorganization that usually accompany such identity changes must be built into the system.

The Problem-Solving System

The second element that characterized the culture produced on Ward H was its problem-solving system. The five characteristics that were abstracted as important to this particular system's functioning were the *provision of support, consistency, discipline, time perspective,* and *mutual regulation* for its members in the pursuit of their common task.

(1) *Provision of Support.* The most basic purpose of this system was to support the efforts of its members in effectively carrying out the purposes of the project. The system's mandate offered goal-direction by prescribing the ultimate task that was to be accomplished—the general problem that was to be solved (i.e., the rehabilitation of chronic schizophrenic patients). In order for the system to function most effectively as a support to its members, certain crucial concepts had to be redefined. *Authority* no longer was defined as the power that one had to coerce, control, or direct others in the performance of assigned tasks; rather it came to mean the capability an individual had to support a subordinate in the use of his

resources to achieve the system's goal. *Responsibility* was defined in terms of the people whose growth one was responsible for, rather than in terms of functions or services. *Accountability* was used to help a subordinate maintain goal-directedness rather than as a method of fixing blame. The application of these three crucial concepts, once redefined, allowed the system to support its members in the pursuit of their goals.

(2) *Consistency.* A second characteristic of the problem-solving system was that of consistency—the extent to which the project was able to keep itself directed by its basic principles and goals. In fact, in this project, the consistent application of principles was substituted for the rigid control of variables which usually characterizes research. Laboratory research, whether or not concerned with people, presets its own conditions and variables. In research efforts for social change usually only goals are preset. In the Ward H project, however, both goals *and* operational principles were preset. The importance of the consistent application of principles lies in the fact that any program dealing with social change constantly confronts choice points. Decisions made at these crucial points affect the eventual success of the programs as well as determine the integrity of the project. In the Ward H research many critical choice points developed, some of which were obvious when they occurred, others of which became apparent only in retrospect. The decisions that were made with the over-all goals of the project in mind, and which in some way elaborated and built upon the original principles, were (seen in retrospect) the most successful decisions.

For example, with the withdrawal of the project directors in the second year, concern was expressed about the ability of the aides to set goals for patients. The alternatives were reduced to having a professionally trained staff set patient goals for the aides or to training the aides in goal-setting skills. The project directors chose the latter, assuming that the aides, though not experienced in goal-setting, were nevertheless competent to do it. To be consistent with the basic principle that the aide was the treatment agent it was necessary that she determine her treatment goals. The result of this decision was the development of an approach to equipping the aides for goal-setting and the subsequent development of positive new dimensions to the project not envisioned in the immediate decision.

Many times the choice was between maintaining the prevailing structure of the experiment or altering it and it was found that compromise at such times usually negated the basic principles and perhaps seriously affected the achievement of the goal.

An example of such a compromise that violated a basic principle concerned the use of project aides on other wards. It is a policy of the institution's nursing service to use aides from one ward to cover another if temporary shortages of personnel occur. The project, in attempting to remain an integral part of the hospital, made the decision to allow such use of its personnel. The breaking of the relationship between Ward H patients and their aides, that occurred whenever the aides were even temporarily transferred out, had a basically detrimental effect upon the project. Such a procedure was inconsistent with the nature of the relationship that had been assumed to be a fundamental need of the patient—an assumption upon which the whole project was based. In other words, although it was sometimes necessary to compromise in a way that worked against the principles of the project, such compromises always had a high price in terms of project effectiveness. Consistency, whenever possible, was the more effective route.

The project's concern with consistency was also focused on the relationship between the goals that it was trying to achieve and the methods that were used in attaining those goals. For example, in carrying out treatment, the supporting staff in its work with the aides focused frequently on the extent to which the means used by the aides were consistent with the goals that they had in mind for the patients. The assumption was that the aide had many means available to her to reach the goals that she had set. The effort of the professional's staff was to help her determine which of these means were most effective (i.e., consistent) in achieving that particular goal.

As another example, in the consulting supervisory process the methods of the supervisor had to be consistent with the goals of the supervision, i.e., the development of the goal-setting competence of the supervisee. If the supervisor were to set a goal for a supervisee, he would in effect be depriving the supervisee of the opportunity to struggle and develop this competency for himself.

(3) *Discipline.* The third characteristic of the problem-solving system was discipline. While the system put a premium on spontaneity and the use of personal style and flexibility, it did not support erratic behavior. It assumed that spontaneity could occur in a disciplined system. Discipline within the system evolved from the notion of a *contract.* Individuals working on a common task consensually set whatever goals they deemed appropriate. The consensual agreement about goals, however, was considered to be a contract among them which could not be unilaterally altered. Such contractual discipline became a project norm and was adhered to rigidly.

An example was the structure of the consulting supervisory process. Basic to the notion of consulting supervision was the fact that the supervisee set goals for himself. The contract was that the supervisor then agreed to hold him accountable for attaining these goals or for their re-evaluation.

Another example of the discipline within the system was adherence to the cognitive structure that the project rested upon. The project used two theoretical models: DesLauriers frame of reference in treatment of patients and the practice of consulting supervision that related to administrative practices. In effect, adherance to these two models was an obligation for all members of the system. While these models were subject to elaboration, any change in them had to be consensual rather than unilateral.

One further example of the discipline implied was that the same ground rules or norms were to apply equally to all members of the system regardless of their level of responsibility, a discipline accepted and followed by aides, supervisors, consultants, and project directors alike.

(4) *Time Perspective.* The fourth characteristic of the problem-solving system was that of time perspective. As one of the goals of the project was the development of the problem-solving competence of its members, it was evi-

dent that the evolvement of this competence required the learning of problem-solving skills and the growth of individual's self-concept as a problem-solver. It was expected that change in this area would require time. Changes in self-concept were not expected to come about immediately.

Conscious efforts were made to lengthen the time perspective of the project's members. For example, the development of the levels system enabled the aides to perceive relatively minor changes in their patients as intermediate steps toward long-range goals.

(5) *Mutual Regulation.* The final characteristic of the system was that of mutual regulation. Lengthening the time perspective served the purpose of permitting more realistic mutual regulation of expectations. In the relationship between the aide and her supervisor, the aide set her own goals and the supervisor held her accountable for them. Under this system the aide soon learned to set goals that were realistic in terms of the time, the energy, and the competence that she had available. As a consequence, the aide generally had a series of success experiences in terms of her own stated aspirations. This is in contrast to a system where the goals are preset by others. In this latter instance the lack of goal attainment is frequently interpreted as personal failure. In the consulting supervisory process, however, when a goal was not reached there was a reconsideration of the appropriateness of the *goal* as well as the methods used. This approach not only insured a minimum of self-derogation, but also reinforced the success experiences through the successive approximation of the goal. An important effect of this process was that it maintained the spirit of optimism in which the project was founded. If such a procedure is working effectively, organizational goals and problem-solving efforts are probably as effective as the system's resources will permit. From the individual's point of view the mutual regulation of goal-setting produces commitment to organizational goals because they are defined as personal goals. *The aspirations of the individual and that of the organization become identical.*

In summary, then, these characteristics maximized the

capabilities of the system by providing support, order, coherence, continuity, and perspective. These characteristics together with the basic attitudes toward people described earlier, permitted a coordinated commitment of the individual's efforts to achieving the program's goals. A problem-solving culture had been generated.

IMPLICATIONS FOR MENTAL HEALTH

The Social System

This project began with a specific treatment problem —that of the chronic schizophrenic patient. Its end result was the evolvement of a social system—a culture. In effect, the social system became the method of treatment, and in view of the results obtained from the project, it is apparent that such an approach is an effective treatment tool. This has been confirmed in other settings, as for example, in the work of Maxwell Jones's therapeutic community.*

In general, the same social system is applied to all patients in mental hospitals despite the fact that they represent a wide variety of treatment problems. The typical mental hospital has a single social system which may best fit the modal needs of its patient population. But the likelihood is that the universal application of any single social system—be it the team approach, the therapeutic community, the custodial approach, or the one described in this work—will be ineffective for a significant proportion of the patients in the typical mental hospital. An institution, thus, may need to permit the development of a variety of social systems. Each *system* would be the institution's method of dealing with a particular type of treatment problem and would be characterized by its own role relationships, administrative practices, and treatment theory consistent with that problem. There would probably be marked differences among the various social systems within a given institution. Within

* Jones, Maxwell, *The Therapeutic Community*, Basic Books, New York, 1953.

such a context, a particular system should be viable only so long as the problem for which it was developed is present. When the problem no longer exists, there is no further need for the system.

Manpower

Another implication of this program has to do with the manpower needs in mental health. Perhaps one of the most critical issues facing mental health programs today is the relative scarcity of professional manpower in the light of the enormity of the task. This problem will continue to exist as long as the underlying assumption is that many years of training are required before one can usefully and constructively relate to troubled individuals. With this assumption in force the demand for services will always exceed the supply of professional manpower.

On the other hand, if one were to assume that social maturity and the potential for growth are the crucial elements in a constructive relationship, the reservoir of available manpower would be immeasurably increased. In the current project the aides were seen as capable of treatment responsibility, not because of their previous training or technical competence, but rather because of their social maturity. This maturity had been demonstrated in their capacity to relate constructively to others in their family and community life. Using this as a basic assumption, the role of the professional thus becomes that of consultant rather than the provider of direct services.

Professional Training

A further implication, relating to the training of the mental health professional, would be to reduce emphasis on the learning of techniques and to increase the emphasis on administrative, consulting, and training skills. With these skills the mental health professional would be in a position to better support the efforts of many coworkers and consequently to have an important effect upon a whole social system. The unit with which such a professional would deal, then, would be the social system rather than the patient. He would in a sense become a social systems architect.

IMPLICATIONS FOR GROWTH-INDUCING
ORGANIZATIONS

Historically within our culture certain social institutions have been entrusted with providing for the growth and development of others. Among these are such institutions as the schools, social welfare organizations, and (more recently) broad social programs such as the national anti-poverty effort. Each of these is based upon certain assumptions about those for whom they are responsible. These basic assumptions are generally reflected in the culture and administrative structure of these social institutions. Although in the course of time the goals of many of the institutions have changed, the administrative structures frequently have not. The old assumptions about people continue to be communicated through these structures despite the fact that these assumptions and attitudes are in opposition to the newer goals of the institution.

For example, social welfare programs began as charities whose purpose was to provide for the needy, the unfortunates, and the paupers of society. Implicit in these charities was the assumption that their charges were in some essential way inferior. Today the goals of most social welfare organizations are the development of the integrity and autonomy of their clients. However, while the goals have changed, many aspects of the administrative and organizational structures have not. Thus, for instance, while the intent of today's Aid to Dependent Children programs is to maintain the integrity of the family unit, the effect is generally acknowledged to be the opposite. This is due, at least in part, to the assumption that a dole is made necessary by the "irresponsibility and failure" of its recipient. Often the legal codes under which this program operates forces the client to demonstrate or "confess" his "irresponsibility" in order to get the funds necessary to function responsibly.

Similarly, in education the goals have changed from "passing information into empty minds" to the development of the student's capacity to problem-solve and to discover. In mental hospitals and prisons, rehabilitation has replaced custody. In all of these, however, the administrative structures and the assumptions upon which they were originally based all too frequently remain unaltered.

Although the intent of such organizations is to promote growth, the structure frequently precludes this. The antiquated legal codes, the authoritarian nature of the hierarchical structure, and the ossification of policies and procedures mitigate against the capability of the individual worker to establish a growth-inducing climate for his clients. Where adaptability is paramount if one is to induce growth in others, the structure of such organizations by their very nature often provides only minimal opportunity for flexibility. When an organization is unable to respond flexibly, one result is often the substitution of symbol for substance. In academic settings, for example, grades rather than learning become the overriding goal. So too in the work setting, status is substituted for growth in personal competence.

An implication of the Ward H project for growth-inducing organizations then is that the test of the adequacy of an administrative structure is the extent to which it supports and facilitates its members in effectively carrying out the goals of the organization. With this project there were no preconceived notions as to what would be the "best" administrative structure. One was permitted to evolve. Each aspect of it was tested in terms of its relevance to the project's goals and assumptions.

A further implication of the Ward H project relates to the response of an organization to the individuality of its members. In contrast to the industrial organization, where conformity may be necessary for results, the effectiveness of growth-inducing organizations rests in large measure upon their ability to evoke the individuality of their members. Through the principle of mutual regulation, individual growth and organizational process are mutually reinforced. If an organization responds to the individual problems of its members, it will become highly variegated through the growth of many autonomous subsystems, each of which attempts to cope with a specific human problem. Perhaps the modern university provides the clearest example of this. Within it one finds many autonomous subsystems—liberal arts colleges, extension services, evening colleges, graduate programs, and professional schools, each of which copes with a unique educational problem and each of which promotes the goal of the university, the education of man.

In growth-inducing organizations, then, a major means available for innovation and change is the development of internally consistent social systems oriented to the solution of particular human problems.

Perhaps one of the most critical issues facing modern man is his relationship to the organizations and social structures made necessary by the increasing interdependence arising from his technical and cultural sophistication. For many the choices seem to be the individualism of Thoreau's *Walden* and the social engineering of Skinner's *Walden II*. The present work assumes no essential incompatibility between the individual and a society geared to his needs.

The alienation and dehumanization men experience in their work currently provides a strong motivation for social change. Many efforts to reverse this dehumanization process have been attempted in recent years. In the Ward H project a social system was permitted to evolve which supported and nurtured a growth-inducing relationship between psychiatric aides and tragically dehumanized patients. Perhaps through its achieved results and their implications it offers a hopeful alternative to the more pervasive problem of alienation and despair.

Appendix A

Behavioral Inventory for Chronic Schizophrenics

I. SPEECH:

A. Verbal Expressiveness:

1.* Occasionally patient will speak one or two words when spoken to, but usually she remains mute.
2. Patient answers with short sentences when spoken to, but doesn't initiate conversations; or patient is constantly chattering or complaining about trivial or bizarre things.
3. Patient initiates conversations and speaks when spoken to, but her speech is usually about some physical complaint, or requests for cigarettes, coffee, etc., and rarely, if ever, does she speak of personal problems such as her family.
4. When patient is bothered by some personal problem talking about it helps and she will seek advice or just talk to you to try and get it off her mind.
5. Patient is able to verbally express her wants, needs, and ideas without difficulty.

B. Structure:

1. Patient's speech is like a riddle, her talking does not help you to understand her needs or wants, i.e., "Fourteenth Street, right turn, since Gabriel sits beside eternal morning."
2. Patient may mimic others' speech or have an excess rhyming in her speech.
3. *Occasionally* the patient tends to confuse you when she speaks. Talks of physical complaints, cigarettes, coffee and what a nice time she had at activities all in the same sentence.
4. Usually the patient expresses herself in a concise and readily understandable manner but occasionally, when

* Number preceding each statement refers to level of behavior.

under stress, will express herself in a roundabout way.
5. Patient expresses herself in a manner which is concise and readily understandable to all.

C. Reliability:

1. Patient's answers or conversations are unpredictable and often bizarre; may say, "Mamma spank, be a good girl," when you say, "Good morning."
2. What the patient tells you doesn't coincide to any degree of accuracy with what has actually taken place. Usually it's a garbled mixture of fact and fancy.
3. Patient is able to give an accurate description of her physiological feelings (says if she is in physical pain or if she feels well), but she cannot be depended on to give an accurate description of her emotional needs or feelings (if she is mad at someone or why she is depressed).
4. What the patient tells you can usually be depended on, but there are times when it can't be depended on, i.e., patient talking about her family to aide may twist the facts to put herself in a more favorable light with the aide.
5. Patient relates with a "normal" degree of accuracy the events and incidents she has experienced.

D. Intensity:

1. Patient *never* speaks in a "normal" tone of voice, but *always* speaks extremely fast or slow and loud or soft and the pitch is of a monotonous quality.
3. *Occasionally*, patient speaks in the same monotonous, whining, angry, loud, soft, slow, or fast voice, but *usually* will speak in a "normal" tone.
5. Patient has appropriate inflexion of speech when angry, happy, or when just conversing and her speech sounds "normal."

E. Non-Verbal Speech:

1. Patient paces hall muttering and mumbling or may scream out incoherently after she has spoken to someone.
3. In non-verbal types of communication, patient will grimace, squint, frown, or shift from foot to foot regardless of the content of her speech.

5. Uses "usual" body and facial expressions to convey her meaning while speaking.

II. ATTENTION SPAN:

A. Duration:

1. Patient appears to be in a "dream-like" state and simply does not focus attention on questions or activity about her.
2. Attention span is extremely short and fluctuates from one moment to the next, i.e., patient takes medication and a moment later is back asking if she can have her medication, or she starts to do something and forgets what it was she was going to do.
3. Patient is able to attend to routine tasks, but attention fluctuates when trying to follow a TV program, playing cards, long conversations, etc.
4. Attention span is unaffected in most situations, but tends to fluctuate when patient is under stress, such as visits from parents, new job, etc.
5. Patient is usually alert, and focuses attention satisfactorily on questions and activity about her even in situations which are stressful for her.

III. ORIENTATION:

A. Person:

1. Patient does not know who or what she is. May think she is a dog, snake, or may react to objects as though they were people.
2. Patient may confuse her identity with aide or other people or may know own name, but is unable to identify herself in a picture, or may refer to herself as "she" or "her" rather than "I," and sign her full name when writing her family.
3. Patient doesn't confuse her identity with others (knows physical self), but is unable to describe her psychological self. Doesn't seem to know much about what kind of person she is, i.e., how smart, if she has a bad temper, is sentimental, etc.
4. Patient knows who she is and has a fairly accurate and consistent idea of what she's like as a person, but doesn't have any clear-cut opinions and attitudes about

events or persons which do not directly affect her personality.

5. Patient has a well-developed, reasonably accurate and stable idea about herself as a separate individual and is able to think of herself as having a particular place or role in relation to her family, to social groups, and to society.

B. Space:

1. Patient does not know where she is. Either has no idea where she is or her answers are bizarre, i.e., says she is in heaven, hell, etc.
2. Patient knows where she is, but gets confused and lost if she goes out by herself out of sight of her home or the hospital.
3. Patient is oriented for nearby outlying areas, but has little conception of directions or distances of places beyond the farm or city where she is living.
4. Patient is oriented for nearby outlying areas and for cities or places where she has been, but has only a general, not too accurate idea about the location of other cities, states, or countries that she has never visited, but which are usually well-known.
5. Patient is oriented for her present location, for nearby outlying areas, and has a good conception of distances and directions of well-known places which are outside of her usual environment.

C. Time:

1. Patient is not oriented in time and doesn't know the date or what time it is, and doesn't seem aware of the passing of time and must be told when to eat, go to bed, etc.
2. Patient may know what time it is (the hour, minute), and that she had visitors yesterday or will see them tomorrow, but patient is unable to experience the passing of time, i.e., may react to things which happened years ago as if they had just occurred or may ask for another cigarette five minutes after she's been told she can't have one for an hour.
3. Patient is oriented for time in the immediate sense (day of week, year, hour, etc.), and can judge, with

a fair degree of accuracy, how long it takes to go uptown so she'll be back in time for dinner, but patient is unable to understand greater lengths of time, such as a week, i.e., may know she's going home for a visit one week from today, but must be reminded to get her clothes together or get ready when the day arrives.

4. Patient is oriented for time in the immediate sense (day of week, year, hour, etc.), and experiences the passing of time in the usual manner in everyday life, but is somewhat hazy about the length of time involved when it comes to dealing with plans for future years or thinking about events which happened years ago.

5. Patient is oriented for time, i.e., knows the hour, day of week, years, and experiences the passing of time in the usual manner, and has an adequate understanding of the length of time involved when dealing with long periods of time, such as a number of years.

IV. APPEARANCE:

A. Use:

1. Patient doesn't attach any significance to her appearance, may refuse to wear any clothes or doesn't care one way or the other what is placed on her.

2. Patient usually has some awareness of her appearance, but frequently looks bizarre, i.e., face is often streaked with lipstick or clothes may be on backwards, or she may tear some of her clothes and go around in rags.

3. The type of clothing patient wears does not seem appropriate for the occasion, i.e., has on a party dress, high heels, carries a large purse in one hand and a mop bucket in the other when she goes to mop floors; or may dress drably and go seeking office work.

4. Although clothing is usually appropriate and she is beginning to formulate some of her own ideas as to what colors suit her best, what type of clothes she wants, she often chooses clothes which are too old or too young for her, or clothes which make her look drab.

5. Patient takes notice of what others are wearing and

has a good idea which style, colors, and type of clothing become her and may discuss this with others for
their opinions.

B. Interest:

1. Aide must attend to patient's personal hygiene or patient would be filthy and unkempt at all times.
2. Patient is able to care for personal hygiene to some
extent. Will do it only if the aide keeps after her and
sometimes gives patient some help with some phase
of it, such as pinning up her hair.
3. Patient has some interest in personal hygiene, but may
wear same dress day after day, bathe infrequently or
patient may be extremely interested in just one phase
of her appearance such as wearing a very nice dress but
being sloppy in the rest of her appearance.
4. Patient is interested in appearance, keeps herself clean
and dresses appropriately and neatly, but is not style
conscious. May wear clothing which is slightly too
old or too young for her.
5. Patient assumes full responsibility and initiative for
personal hygiene. Dresses in a fashion which is becoming and acceptable to her.

C. Body Position:

1. Has a "waxy flexibility" about her much of the time;
postures, or if arm is raised she will hold this position
for long periods of time.
2. Body posture is either rigid or is a pose that she assumes, i.e., usually sits on the edge of chair rather than
relaxing in it or will stand in an affected pose of relaxation but arms and body are tense.
3. Posture is usually appropriate for the occasion, but
may assume poses when she sees you looking at her.
4. Posture is usually appropriate and normal, but under
stress may tend to slouch or become tense posturally.
5. Posture of the patient appears relaxed or "normal" and
usually her posture is good.

D. Facial Expression:

1. Patient has a "blank," "expressionless," "empty" look
about her most of the time, even in situations where

you would expect some expression, such as when she seems to have experienced something intensely.

2. While patient may express more than one emotion by facial expression she usually looks like one of the following most of the time: angry, depressed, confused, silly, preoccupied, worried, etc., or her expressions change rapidly for no apparent reason, extreme anger one minute, relative calm the next.

3. Patient's facial expressions are occasionally inappropriate for the matter being discussed. Looks worried, has a guarded or suspicious look when discussing small events such as washing clothes, going to town, etc.

4. Facial expressions are appropriate for the subject matter, but these expressions may be slightly under- or overdone, i.e., looks overly sad when hearing mildly depressing news.

5. Patient appears alert and her facial expressions have appropriate amount of warmth and meaning attached to them.

V. PERFORMANCE:

A. Skill and Quality:

1. Patient must be "looked after" like a child, i.e., must be bathed, clean clothes laid out for her, helped with dressing, etc.

2. Patient does not seem to have the skills necessary to do familiar routine tasks such as: scrubbing floors, washing dishes, making beds, etc., but is able to care for immediate needs such as dressing, bathing, eating, etc., with supervision.

3. Patient has the skill necessary to do familiar routine tasks, i.e., scrubbing floors, washing dishes, making beds, etc., but has great difficulty in learning how to do new tasks.

4. Patient has the skill necessary to perform most familiar and new tasks, but requires occasional supervision.

5. Patient is efficient and versatile in her work, i.e., does routine tasks well and new tasks with a minimum of explanation.

B. Endurance:

1. Patient will do nothing without constant urging and someone else must always be present, if she is to be kept at her task.
2. Patient requires frequent urging to do tasks and often leaves work incompleted.
3. Patient works in spurts, i.e., works well one time without being told and won't the next time she is asked, and/or does well only those tasks that she likes to do.
4. Patient regularly does all of her work, but has constant complaints and gripes about doing it, and occasionally may try to get out of doing what she is supposed to do.
5. Patient regularly does all of her work well and does not complain unduly about doing it.

C. Purpose or Use:

1. Patient's activities and actions are bizarre or meaningless and her explanation of her actions is senseless.
2. Patient's activities and actions seem appropriate until she explains what she is doing, i.e., says, "All these little articles of clothing I made for the mice on the ward."
3. Patient attempts to carry out activities or tasks in a logical fashion and knows what she is doing but gets bogged down in the process so she may do the same thing over and over, or go from one thing to another without getting anything done.
4. Patient's activities and actions and understanding of what she's doing are appropriate, but she seems somewhat inefficient so it takes longer and/or more effort to accomplish anything than it should.
5. Patient's activities and actions are easily understood by others and by herself. Tasks are efficiently carried out.

D. Effect:

1. Patient is uninterested and incapable of doing even simple tasks and she must be cared for by aides or other patients.
2. Patient is capable of doing simple tasks and shows interest in things she wants to do but her attitude is so

hostile that she will not cooperate or give in to instructions from others.

3. Patient can and will do most ward tasks, but will do so only if she sees an immediate reward.

4. Patient does things for herself without urging, but will not help others, says "You're just trying to use me."

5. Patient enjoys her work, i.e., appears happy when she has a job to do and if she doesn't have a job will try to find something to do or someone to help.

VI. MOTOR CONTROL:

A. Degree:

1. Patient has little control over her motor behavior, but there is nothing physically wrong, i.e., patient is usually unsteady on her feet, falls an unusual number of times, is always dropping objects, etc.

2. Patient moves around in a mechanical or quite deliberate way, i.e., patient appears to put forth great amounts of effort and concentration while moving from place to place, and/or may have noticeable tremors (shaking of hands, arms, head, legs) much of the time, not due to physical causes or reactions to drugs.

3. Patient has control over gross bodily movements, such as walking, movement of arms, head, etc., but sometimes she can't manipulate small objects very well, such as pencils, eating utensils, and/or may show slight tremors while sewing, eating, fastening her dress, etc.

4. Patient's motor behavior is "normal" except sometimes when she encounters stressful situations or topics, her hands may flutter about, she may be prone to drop things, or become slightly awkward.

5. Patient's motor movements appear "normal" in all respects, i.e., gross bodily movements and fine movements such as finger manipulations are unimpaired unless there is a physical reason.

B. Quality:

1. Patient's motor activity is frequently aimless and only expressive of severe tension and disturbance, i.e., gestures wildly, or makes certain movements over and over in ritualistic fashion.

2. Patient's motor activity is usually without purpose, i.e., pill rolling (rubbing thumb and forefinger back and forth constantly), picking at skin until she bleeds, continually opening and closing mouth, etc.

3. Patient's motor activity is *usually* purposeful and appropriate for the situation, but when upset she goes through excessive motion in doing something, or moves quite slowly or rapidly, or shows odd mannerisms, i.e., repeatedly tugging at hair, making certain motions with hands each time she speaks, etc.

4. Patient's motor activity is purposeful and appropriate, *but* on rare occasions, under extreme stress, patient may go through excessive motions or become extremely inactive.

5. Patient's motor activity (movement of arms, legs, hands, etc.), is purposeful and appropriate to patient's intent, i.e., patient does not make aimless motions or movements, or move unusually slowly or rapidly, or show odd mannerisms, i.e., repeatedly tugging at hair, making certain motions with hands every time she speaks, etc.

VII. *BODY RHYTHMS:*

A. Degree:

1. Patient leads vegetative existence, and body temperature may vary for no apparent reason, or she may show little response to heat, pain, etc., as when the bath water is very hot or when she hurts herself.

2. Patient's body rhythms (sleeping, eating, elimination, menstrual, etc.) are disrupted so that one or more are severely disordered, i.e., patient may have to be tube fed, may be incontinent, or may skip menstrual periods, etc., without physical cause.

3. Patient's body rhythms (sleeping, eating, elimination, menstrual, etc.) are disrupted so that one or more are *moderately* disordered, i.e., patient may not be able to sleep well without sedation, may have unusual eating habits in regard to quantities and/or preferences, or patient may flush or sweat excessively, etc., without physical basis.

4. Patient's body rhythms (sleeping, eating, elimination,

menstrual) are not unusual, but she may have minor difficulties with constipation, diarrhea, indigestion, etc.
5. Patient's body rhythms (sleeping, eating, elimination, menstrual, etc.) are not unusual and do not vary much from "normal" without physical cause.

B. Stability:
1. Patient's body rhythms (sleeping, eating, elimination, menstrual, etc.) are disordered for long periods of time, i.e., weeks to months at a time without physical basis, i.e., patient may have to be tube fed for weeks, may be incontinent for weeks to months, may skip one or more menstrual periods, etc.
2. Patient's body rhythms (sleeping, eating, elimination) are often irregular without physical basis for days, or a week at a time. She may eat great quantities or no food at all for several days in a row or she may have extremely irregular menstrual periods.
3. Patient's body rhythms (sleeping, eating, elimination, menstrual, etc.) are usually not disordered without physical cause, but she tends to have bodily reactions when something unusual is going on at home or on the ward, i.e., patient will not eat for a day or two after coming back from home visit, may have diarrhea whenever she leaves the hospital, etc.
4. Patient's body rhythms (sleeping, eating, elimination, menstrual, etc.) are rarely disordered, but she tends to be quite concerned with her bodily functions and frequently has minor complaints although there is nothing physically wrong.
5. Patient's body rhythms (sleeping, eating, elimination, menstrual, etc.) are usually "normal" and patient is not unusually concerned over bodily functions.

VIII. INTERACTION:

A. Isolation (Degree of):
1. Patient is very withdrawn, i.e., patient sits by herself, will not speak or acknowledge another's presence.
2. Patient will not acknowledge your presence unless you force yourself on her, i.e., taking hold of her shoulder

and calling her by name, nor will patient enter into any form of activity unless you "push" her.

3. Patient is a "lone wolf" type who will talk briefly with others but would rather be by herself and usually she is found off to one side of the groups watching what they are doing rather than participating in the activities herself.

4. Patient will take part in ward work and social events, but has only one or two friends.

5. Patient has several friends, and actively engages in ward work and social events, and is able to get others to join her in work and play.

B. Awareness:

1. Patient doesn't seem to differentiate between objects and people, i.e., treats objects as if they were people, may talk to a letter or curse a chair, and may not register recognition of people, or may push them out of her path.

2. Patient seems to have no interest in and/or regard for other people, i.e., she may turn away from others unless she wants something, or may hit at others for little reason.

3. Patient frequently watches others with guarded interest or apprehension and easily misinterprets requests and others' behavior, or may try to take over activities, conversations, etc., and boss others without regard for their rights or feelings.

4. Patient seems interested in only those people who have some importance to her own life and welfare and remains indifferent to what's happening to others she knows.

5. Patient responds to people and objects appropriately and comprehends and reacts to the feelings and problems of others in a "normal" way.

C. Effect:

1. Patient occupies same spot on ward most of her waking hours and makes no attempt to interact with others, nor do others make any attempt to talk or engage her in activities.

2. Patient makes others feel "uneasy" in her presence. Patient may break furniture, destroy objects, is unpredictable.
3. Patient rejects or is rejected by most of the other patients, i.e., usually if she doesn't bother them they don't bother her.
4. Patient is acknowledged and tolerated by others and is usually included in group activities, but is picked by only one or two as a friend.
5. Patient is usually active in groups, may be recognized by others as a leader, and is chosen by several as a friend.

IX. DELUSIONS:

A. Effect:

1. Patient is constantly preoccupied with delusional material and cannot speak, do simple tasks, or care for her physical needs without constant supervision.
2. Most of the patient's thoughts and conversations are colored by her delusional ideas, but she is able to care for her basic physical needs without much difficulty.
3. Despite delusional material frequently appearing in patient's conversation she is still able to carry out familiar tasks and enter into many activities.
4. Although patient seems to have some mildly unusual ideas about sex, work, mental illness, etc., there are no obvious delusional thoughts which might hamper her in holding a job away from the hospital if support is given to her.
5. Patient does not seem to display any signs of delusional material.

B. Content:

1. Patient has strong persistent delusions of persecution, i.e., believes others are trying to attack or poison her or may have delusions of grandiose nature, believes she is a very powerful and famous person.
2. Delusional material is such that patient is obnoxious or threatening in her manner, but rarely does she try to harm others, i.e., believes she is being held unnecessarily or that someone is trying to get her money.
3. Patient is not delusional, but does have some ideas

of reference, i.e., believes others are always looking at her, an aide or relative is checking up on her, etc.

4. Patient isn't delusional or markedly suspicious, but may be mildly suspicious and "touchy" on one or two subjects.

5. Patient does not seem to have any delusional thoughts or odd ideas and she reacts to all situations in a "normal" manner.

X. HALLUCINATIONS:

A. Type:

1. Patient has visions of people trying to harm her, may hear these visions telling her to do acts of violence and will constantly and actively hallucinate regardless of her surroundings.

2. Patient actively hallucinates, but tries to keep this from others; may occasionally act on her hallucinations.

3. Patient doesn't admit having hallucinations and attempts to explain away any such experiences as being something dreamed, imagined, etc.

4. Patient seems completely free of hallucinations, but under stress in a crisis, she may assume a listening or watchful attitude as if she might be hearing or seeing something.

5. Patient seems completely free from hallucinations.

B. Effect:

1. Patient's hallucinations are such as to be dangerous to self and others, i.e., feels that someone or something is trying to harm her and she is very unpredictable and may try to injure herself or others, or she may become completely withdrawn and preoccupied with her hallucinations.

2. Patient appears extremely frightened by or clearly influenced by her hallucinations, but does not take action on them or become completely withdrawn, i.e., she usually sits quietly but will respond to others or go back to work when given support.

3. Patient is not preoccupied by hallucinations, but occasionally shows sudden lapses in behavior due to the intrusion of hallucinations.

4. Patient does not give any clear evidence that she has

hallucinations, but under stress may show momentary lapses in behavior which seem caused by fleeting hallucinatory experiences.
5. Patient does not give any evidence that would indicate she has hallucinations.

XI. EMOTION:

A. Quality:

1. Patient shows emotions inappropriately, may seem incapable of expressing any emotion or may express tremendous outbursts of emotion for just a few minutes, may begin crying while she is eating, or laughs or giggles at depressing news.
2. Patient "follows" other people's reactions and imitates their emotion, i.e., if another person is laughing the patient starts laughing too.
3. Patient's expression of emotion is somewhat stilted, artificial, or overdone. A small incident may lead to an angry explosion, or something mildly humorous may be reacted to with loud and long laughter.
4. Patient's emotions usually seem genuine and appropriate, but under stress, expression of emotions may become temporarily "flattened" or emotional reactions may seem momentarily exaggerated.
5. Patient's emotions are genuine and appropriate, i.e., she doesn't try to imitate others but is capable of expressing her own true feelings. If angry at someone she tells them so, if happy or confused over something she expresses herself to them.

B. Degree of:

1. Patient's emotional reactions don't seem appropriate for the reality situation, i.e., shows little reaction when you expect some emotional response or shows extreme reaction to trivial matters.
2. Patient's emotional reactions frequently do not seem appropriate for the reality situation so she may show little reaction when you expect some emotional response or show extreme reaction to trivial matters. i.e., patient sits and does nothing while another patient destroys her belongings; or may get extremely angry when she can't find her knitting needle.
3. Patient reacts emotionally to only those things which

affect her personally, i.e., does not display fear for others' safety, happiness for others' good fortune, anger for others when they have been unduly wronged, etc.

4. Patient usually reacts appropriately emotionally to things which affect her personally, but gets overinvolved in affairs of others or while being aware of what's happening to those close to her, doesn't seem to feel anything about it.

5. Patient reacts in a mature and generally "normal" manner to situations which confront her, i.e., patient knows how she feels when she is happy, sad, angry, and is able to share another patient's joys, sorrows, etc.

C. Control:

1. Emotional outbursts are common with this patient and she is completely unable to control herself at these times and must be physically restrained and controlled by aides.

2. When patient becomes angry or depressed, she remains in this mood, cannot be pulled out of it by her aide, may require medication, or ECT, or seclusion to stop the "mood."

3. Patient still needs a simple, unchanging routine and the presence of the aide to help her control her emotions. When she becomes upset, or loses temper, a few words from the aide will calm her down. However, patient will occasionally express feelings of losing control, or will in some way ask aide to help her control herself.

4. Patient can control her emotions fairly well, but occasionally may get a little shaky in situations which are stressful for her.

5. Patient is able to control her emotions most of the time and usually expresses emotions in an appropriate manner.

XII. SEX:

A. Object Choice:

1. Patient shows no sexual interest whatsoever or may openly masturbate a great deal, or make masturbatory movements much of the time.

2. Patient's choice of sex object may be bizarre, i.e., seems unable to distinguish between people and objects and frequently directs her sexual feelings toward a doll or some other inappropriate object, or may direct her sexual feelings toward an imaginary person.
3. Patient seems interested in sexual matters (although she may avoid any kind of sexual or social contact), but at some time makes one feel she may have some homosexual problems, i.e., spends time exclusively with a patient of same sex. May kiss, hug, and pet other patients or aide in a seductive way.
4. Patient's interest in sex is restricted to men, but is uncertain of self with men. May either get "nervous" and "shaky" when around men or may overdo it by being too aggressive with men.
5. Patient's actions, dress, appearance, etc., are appropriate for her sex, i.e., wears female attire, makeup, and generally her interests are directed toward the home or feminine occupation and is appropriately interested in men.

B. Role:
1. Patient shows no awareness of being a woman. Shows no interest in feminine clothing, activities, etc. Does feminine things only because aide tells her or makes her do so.
2. Patient seems to have some slight awareness of being a woman, but is highly disturbed by this or handles it inappropriately through denial, clumsy experimentation or exaggeration of feminine activities, interests and sexual behavior.
3. Patient is aware of being a woman and is clumsily struggling with accepting it or learning to carry out the role. Seems very uncomfortable and awkward with feminine interests and around men; reacts to this in an intense, but not inappropriate manner.
4. Patient is well aware she is a woman and is trying to live comfortably with all aspects of the feminine role, i.e., maternal interests, being a wife, feminine interests and activities, but may have difficulty or be unsure of self in one or more of these areas.
5. Patient seems to be comfortable with idea of being a

woman and handles the feminine role appropriately and in her own way.

C. Control:

1. Patient shows no evidence of feeling that she is a woman. Shows no preference for feminine clothing, activities, etc. Does feminine things only because aide tells her or makes her do so. Sexual activity is either non-existent or restricted to bizarre.

2. Patient shows little evidence of being able, on her own, to control her sexual behavior. At times patient may act out sexually and have to be restricted to the ward or put in seclusion.

3. When around aide, patient has no problems in managing control of sexual behavior; however, when away from aide (i.e., at evening activities, in Quonteen, on the grounds), patient often feels threatened by or shaky about her own sexual impulses or the impulses of others.

4. Patient generally able to handle and control own sexual impulses, but occasionally when outside the hospital and on her own may get uncomfortable about sexuality and may become unsure of her control.

5. Patient seems able to appropriately control sexual impulses in own way and doesn't seem threatened by them.

Appendix B

Quantitative Scoring System for BRL Object Sorting Test and Draw-a-Person Test

BRL Object Sorting Test

The BRL Sorting Test is described in Rapaport's *Diagnostic Psychological Testing, Vol. I.* The scoring system used followed the method outlined in Rapaport. However, inasmuch as this scoring system is a qualitative or descriptive one, it was necessary to devise a quantitative scoring system so the test results could be handled statistically.

Scoring of sorting is based on both adequacy of the verbal response and the extent of the conceptual span. Scoring of Verbalization on both the Active and Passive parts of the test is based on both adequacy and conceptual level.

1. *Scoring of Conceptual Span:* Rapaport's scoring categories [N, (N), n, + 1, (L), L] were assigned weights. The more deviant the span of the sort the lesser the weight; the more appropriate, the higher the weight.

N	(N)	n	+	1	(L)	L
0	3	5	7	5	3	0

A. Special scoring problems relating to conceptual span:

(1) Double attributes, e.g., red and round, were scored as N;
(2) Double scoring situations, e.g., N + L sort, received the average of the scores.

2. *Scoring of Verbalization:* Points were assigned Rapaport's scoring categories as follows: 0—No Credit Responses; 1 or 2—Limited Credit Responses; 3—Concrete

Definition; 5—Functional Definition; 7—Conceptual
Definition.

A. No credit responses:
   (1) Failure (no response, clearly inadequate responses
       and/or inappropriate responses);
   (2) True symbolic responses;
   (3) Fabulation with inferences;
   (4) Grossly fabulated responses without inferences;
   (5) Grossly syncretistic responses;
   (6) All chain responses;
   (7) Multiple split/narrow responses (more than two
       groups);
   (8) Combination of two or more of limited credit
       responses.

B. Limited credit responses = 1 point:
   (1) Inadequate verbalization with some glimmer of a
       correct or appropriate idea;
   (2) Concrete verbalization in which significance of
       no more than one object changed but not in a
       symbolic way, e.g., disc or sink stopper interpreted
       as coaster, ashtray, hot pad, etc.;
   (3) Simple split/narrow responses (no more than two
       appropriate groups with each group containing two
       or more objects);
   (4) Simple syncretistic response based on location or
       derivation;
   (5) Simple fabulized response without inferences (no
       more than two instances of fabulization which
       have logical relevance per response).

C. Special scoring problems relating to verbalized responses:
   (1) Definition correct but verbalization mildly in-
       adequate = 1 point;
   (2) Combination or alternative responses = average
       of scores;
   (3) Responses improved without help beyond indirect
       questioning = highest obtained score;

(4) A good definition partly spoiled = 2 points;
(5) A good response followed by a poor response = average of scores;
(6) False conceptual definition = 2 points.

Total Score: The total score for the test was arrived at as follows:

Conceptual Span; Active Sort = Possible   49
Verbalization; Active Sort = Possible   49
Total for Active Sort = Possible   98
Verbalization; Passive Sort = Possible   84
Total for BRL Test = Possible   182

It was found that the assigning of numerical scores was relatively simple after the sortings and verbalizations had been scored using the conventional qualitative scoring method. No special questions or problems arose when two clinicians administered and scored some BRL Sorting Tests in the same way. For purposes of statistical analysis the total scores for Part I and Part II were both used separately. These two scores were not combined as an inspection of the scores suggested that adding them together might obscure possible significant differences in functioning on the two parts of the test.

Draw-a-Person Test

Each patient was asked to make three figure drawings as part of the test battery. The "usual" instructions were given to draw a picture of a person—the whole person. After completing the first drawing, the patient was told to draw a picture of a person of the opposite sex. Ordinarily, the female patients first drew a picture of a woman so that in most instances the second drawing was of a male. For the third drawing, the patient was asked to draw a picture of herself. Quantitative scoring of the drawings was approached in two different ways in an effort to "capture" and record as much information as possible from the patients' productions relevant to their relative level of functioning and degree of disorganization.

One scoring method used was the Goodenough Drawing-of-a-Man system which assigns points on the basis of the content included in a drawing and to a limited extent the adequacy of presentation. No attempt was made to use the Goodenough scoring as an index of intelligence. The total score, consisting of the sum of points earned on the first figure drawing, was the measure used. It was initially included as the range of scores suggested that it would differentiate among patients. A check on the reliability of the score was made by scoring the male and female figure drawings done at the same point in time by a small group of randomly selected patients. Inspection revealed usually only a few total score points difference. This suggested that the patients generally were quite consistent about the number and manner of presentation of details of body and clothing included at any one time.

The second scoring method used to analyze the figure drawings was a system devised to take account of some of the major qualitative factors reflected by the patients' figure drawings. Attention was directed toward an analysis of those aspects of the drawings which seem more general and universal in order to provide a consistent basis for at least a gross evaluation of a patient's level of functioning. The D-A-P qualitative factors selected for examination were: The relationship of a drawing to paper space (this included taking into account the approximate size and placement of a drawing), the quality of movement suggested by a drawing (here attention is directed to the posture and apparent motility suggested), the relative presence or absence of detail including specific areas of emphasis or lack of detail, the presence of remarkable qualitative and/or inappropriate aspects of a drawing— as a whole and as to details, the relative adequacy of body parts and the relationship between them, and the quality of lines as to pressure, continuity and type of lines drawn.

Each of the three figure drawings drawn by a patient as part of a test battery was examined and scored for the seven qualitative factors abbreviated as concerning placement, size, movement, detail, remarkable aspects, relative adequacy, and lines. The scoring involved use of a five point rating scale for each of the factors. General scoring criteria in descriptive terms were formulated for each of the five steps or levels for each of the seven qualitative factors so that all the patients' figure drawings could be analyzed in the same way.

D-A-P Qualitative Scoring Scales*

1. PLACEMENT
   A. Figure not bounded by paper limits or uses only a corner of paper (usually upper left), as though the rest of the paper didn't exist.
   B. Figure not fully contained by paper limits, though drawing as a whole reflects efforts at staying within limits.
   C. Figure is drawn in such a way that any of its extremities are placed at or very near limit of the paper, or is confined to one quadrant.
   D. Figure is placed completely to one side or other of the paper, or is confined to top or bottom half of paper.
   E. Figure is fairly well centered on paper—within middle $\frac{1}{3}$ of paper space and margin of space is left at top and bottom of paper.

2. SIZE
   A. Figure is very large covering practically all the paper, or is very small covering only a fraction of the area of the paper (height less than $\frac{1}{4}$ of paper or width less than $\frac{1}{10}$).
   B. Figure has exceptional dimensions in relation to the paper, either quite large (height obviously more than $\frac{3}{4}$ of the paper, or width obviously more than $\frac{1}{3}$), or quite small (height less than $\frac{1}{3}$ of paper, or width less than $\frac{1}{8}$).
   C. Figure is drawn in such a way in relation to the paper so that its width is disproportionate to its height or vice-versa.
   D. Figure, though drawn with height and width in proper proportions, is slightly too large (height

* Same scoring standards apply for busts or incomplete figures.

between ⅔ and ¾ of paper, or width between ¼ and ⅓ of paper), or slightly too small (height between ⅓ and ½ of paper, or width between ⅛ and ⅙) in relation to the paper.

E. Figure as a whole of average size in relation to the paper and drawn with height and width in proper proportions (height between ½ and ⅔ of paper, and width between ¼ and ⅙).

3. MOVEMENT

A. Figure drawn in such a way it appears to be fluid or figure fragmented.

B. Figure appears rigid and immobilized or suspended in space, or figure incomplete despite directions.

C. Figure appears to be standing at odd angle or peculiar way or seems to be moving in a bizarre fashion.

D. Figure appears to be correctly aligned and oriented in all respects except feet go in opposite direction to body so maintaining balance or movement such as walking would be impossible.

E. Figure appears to be correctly aligned and oriented in all respects so it seems to be standing or moving in natural realistic manner.

4. DETAIL

A. Figure is missing major body parts or features so that features are grossly incomplete or representation of head or trunk is omitted, or several other body parts are omitted, or figure contains several bizarre details, distortions, displacements, or peculiar, extraneous elaborations.

B. Figure includes major body parts and features in simple form, but otherwise is empty, or one feature, or one body part other than the head or trunk is omitted including indication of hands where appropriate, or figure includes one or two peculiar details, or distortions, or displacements, or unusual elaborations of body parts or dress.

C. Figure includes major body parts and features but may omit minor details of features and/or of hands, or may be complete except for feet or some indication of hair and/or of ears where appropriate, or little attention has been given to shape of trunk (or to clothing), or figure includes many details on body and/or of dress which while not bizarre, appear excessive.

D. Figure includes major body parts and features, but may omit one minor detail of features such as lack of pupils or empty pupils, or may only roughly indicate feet or may show hair and/or fingers in simple fashion; figure may include relatively few details of dress and/or have little shape to body or figure may include a minor distortion, or an area of the figure or the clothing may be given unusual, but not peculiar, emphasis or elaboration.

E. Figure includes major body parts and features, includes the expected minor details of features, and essentially complete and appropriate detail on body parts and dress.

5. REMARKABLE ASPECTS

A. Figure as a whole is very simple and primitive and/or asymmetrical, or boundaries of figure are vague, or distinction between body parts and clothing is confused, or figure appears very weird.

B. Head and/or body of figure have gross irregularities in outline or are quite asymmetrical, or one or more features and/or parts of trunk are grossly displaced or omitted, or figure and/or clothing appear odd, or arms and/or legs omitted, linear, or only grossly suggested.

C. Arms and/or legs of figure have obvious irregularities in outline or are quite asymmetrical or are clearly displaced or incomplete, or figure contains transparencies, or figure and/or clothing includes odd lapses or discrepancies and/or hands and feet omitted or only grossly suggested, or figure appears to be of young child.

D. Hands and feet of figure have obvious irregularities or are quite asymmetrical or incomplete, or body is shapeless or quite exaggerated, or clothing and/or hair clearly reflect confusion over sexual identification, or figure appears to be prepubescent, or figure contains one or two minor lapses or discrepancies.

E. Figure is essentially complete drawing of teenager or adult and contains no obvious irregularities, distortions, asymmetrical parts or discrepancies. Drawing may contain one or two minor errors or omissions, e.g., apposition of thumb omitted or incorrect, omission of eyebrows, or sleeves, or of hands when they appear purposively concealed behind back or in pockets, etc.

6. RELATIVE ADEQUACY

A. *Head* is simple circle or peculiar in shape or way out of proportion; *trunk* is simple in shape, linear, circular, oval, triangular, etc., omitted, or way out of proportion; *features* are very simple or crude or peculiar, or way out of proportion or grossly incomplete; no *clothing* is indicated or clothing is transparent *and* peculiar emphasis is given to anatomical detail.

B. *Head* is obviously too large or small or obviously asymmetrical, or parts of head are out of proportion, or no hair indicated; *trunk* is too large or small or obviously asymmetrical, or parts of body are out of proportion; *features* are odd or distorted, or clearly asymmetrical, or out of proportion, or one feature is missing, or grossly incomplete; no *clothing* indicated or clothing style is bizarre; *arms and/or legs* are omitted, linear, or grossly suggested.

C. *Head* is slightly too large or small or asymmetrical, or hair is limited to circumference or is crudely sketched; *trunk* is slightly too large or small or asymmetrical; *features* are slightly but noticeably too large or small or asymmetrical, or include little detail; *clothing* indicated by outline or buttons or one line or clothing style is odd; *arms and/or legs* are too short or long or oddly shaped, or quite irregular or asymmetrical, or have no joints; *hands and/or feet* omitted or only grossly suggested.

D. *Head* may deviate slightly from oval shape; *trunk*

may be straight or slightly exaggerated in shape; *features* may include one minor omission or error; *clothing* consists of two or three articles simply indicated, or clothing style is slightly odd or exaggerated; *arms and/or legs* may be shapeless, or slightly out of proportion or slightly irregular or asymmetrical; *hands and/or feet* may be too large or oddly shaped, or quite irregular or asymmetrical or incomplete.

E. *Head, trunk* and *features* are essentially complete, adequate, appropriate, and in proportion; *clothing* should be complete without incongruities, but may include one minor discrepancy; *arms and/or legs* may include one minor error; *hands and/or feet* may be slightly out of proportion, or slightly irregular, or asymmetrical, or include one or two minor errors, or omissions.

7. LINES

A. Lines are fragmented or disjointed, or are quite uncoordinated, or appear very rigid or fluid, and pressure of lines is usually very light, heavy, or quite variable.

B. Some lines are broken, leave gaps, or lines may involve excessive sketching, shading, or much overlapping, or atypical closures, or some lines are uncoordinated, or appear rigid, or exaggerated, and pressure of lines may be slightly but noticeably light, heavy, or variable.

C. Lines are usually continuous, but a few lines may have small breaks or gaps, or some involve excessive sketching, shading, or overlapping, or lines look constricted or awkwardly drawn, and pressure of lines is generally moderate and not remarkable.

D. Lines are usually continuous and well-coordinated, but may include one or two minor discrepancies involving sketching, shading, overlapping, or atypical joinings, and pressure of line is generally moderate.

E. Lines are usually continuous and well-coordinated, are generally firm but not rigid, include no discrepancies, and pressure of lines is generally moderate.

After the scoring system for the qualitative factors was devised, a sample of thirty drawings, three drawings by each of ten patients, was scored independently by two clinicians. Discrepancies were discussed and resolved and a few changes were then made to clarify some of the scoring criteria. Then, a second reliability check was made using another sample of thirty drawings which had been pulled, ordered and identifying data disguised by a third person. The scores assigned by the two scorers for the seven qualitative factors were correlated using the rho rank-difference method and a one-tailed table was used to determine levels of significance. The results are presented in the table below.

RESULTS OF RELIABILITY STUDY OF QUALITATIVE SCORING OF FIGURE DRAWINGS
Rho Correlations and Levels of Significance

Qualitative Factor	1st Drawing Rho	P	2nd Drawing Rho	P	3rd Drawing Rho	P
Placement	.85	<.01	.89	<.01	.94	<.01
Size	.53	>.05	.79	<.01	.48	>.05
Movement	.35	>.05	.79	<.01	.69	<.05
Detail	.81	<.01	.93	<.01	.85	<.01
Remarkable Aspects	.64	<.05	.93	<.01	.94	<.01
Relative Adequacy	.97	<.01	.99	<.01	.94	<.01
Lines	−.02	>.05	.73	<.01	.69	<.05

The table shows that all but four of the twenty-one correlations were significant at the .05 level or better. Two of the four non-significant correlations concerned scoring "size" and here it was possible to identify the main source of difference and to make the scoring directions more explicit. The discrepancy between scorers on the movement factor for the first drawing appeared due to a consistent difference in evaluating the relative rigidity of a figure drawing. The lack of agreement on scoring for lines on the first drawing seemed primarily due to one scorer rating line quality on a higher level than the other.

However, in general, the second reliability check reflected a high level of agreement between two scorers familiar with the qualitative scoring system.

Appendix C

Changes in Edwards Personal Preference Schedule Profiles of Individual Aides

A$_1$* There are a large number of changes in this profile. One of the most significant appears to be an increased sensitivity and awareness of the feelings and motives of others and a marked drop in self-centeredness. She appears to have been extremely concerned with herself and on the egocentric side. However, her post-profile indicates definite reductions in this area. She is much more sensitive to people. Along with this, she appears to be much freer and less concerned with conformity and doing what the system demands. This is reflected by her lowered deference score. In addition to this, her need for autonomy has also gone up. This tends to indicate that she has a stronger need for independence, is probably more self-confident, has a stronger need to make her own decisions and is bothered less by traditions, norms, and past practices. Along with this, there has been an increase in her achievement need and a slight reduction in her need for succorance. Furthermore, she is far less concerned with very routine details of a minute and trivial nature.

A$_2$ Basically, there are really no significant changes in this profile. There are just general trends. The most significant trends are a drop in her need for order and for concerning herself with detail and a slight increase in her ability to assume a supervisory role. She also appears to be slightly more sensitive to the needs and feelings of others.

B$_1$ The most significant changes in this profile are the increased scores on the autonomy and exhibition scales and the decrease in succorance. This indicates that

* The coding system used to identify the aides is as follows: letters A through D indicate the four aide pairs. The number 1 indicates the morning shift aide in each pair and the 2 the afternoon shift aide. Profiles appear beginning on p. 240.

this aide has a much stronger need for independence
and is more self-reliant and possibly more self-assured.
The increase in her exhibition score suggests that she
is much more outgoing and that she is probably more
self-confident in interpersonal situations. Along with
her increased need for independence, she has less need
for constant reinforcement, praise, and encouragement
from others. The fact that her aggression score is the
same both for pre and post, that her deference is low,
and that there is an increase in her autonomy suggests that she has been and is probably still somewhat
of a supervisory problem. She appears to be somewhat
of a maverick. However, instead of expressing her aggressiveness in a rather passive, dependent fashion, she
now is much more open and above-board. The fact that
her autonomy and exhibition scores went up and her
succorance score down also suggests that her image
of herself has probably changed in the positive direction.

B_2 The most striking change in this aide is the very
strong development of a need for dominating others,
for supervising people, for making group decisions, and
for having a position which will give her more prestige
and respect. There is also a significant decrease in her
need for change. She appears to be much happier in
situations which are routine and repetitive and has
much less of a need for variety and constant change.
There has also been a significant loosening in terms of
her interpersonal relationships. Her post-profile indicates that she is much more outgoing, spontaneous, and
informal. She also appears to be more helpful and
warm. This is reflected by the increase in her exhibition, affiliation and nurturance scores. She appears to
be more spontaneous and informal in interpersonal situations. Furthermore, she appears to be less deferent
and less critical and resentful. There is also a definite
lessening in her need for autonomy, but this appears
to reflect the fact that she is far less rebellious, resentful, and critical. This is reflected by the fact that her
aggression score went down along with her autonomy
score. Her pre-profile indicates that she was probably
passively rebellious and defiant, and her post-profile sug-

gests that she is much more constructive in expressing feelings of resentment. It also appears that she is less dependent and slightly more self-confident and self-assured.

C_1 This aide shows little in the way of any significant changes. In all probability she was somewhat of a problem person. She is extremely critical, argumentative, rebellious, and needful. It is possible that these characteristics were very much ingrained and that positive growth was very difficult to obtain. If anything, she manifested some regressions. Her need for succorance increased, and her concern for detail and her persistence dropped to levels which suggest that she had considerable difficulty organizing herself efficiently. She appears to be so tied up with her own needs and with her anger that she really has difficulty cathecting to her environment. One slight change might be the fact that her criticalness-argumentativeness may have gone underground as reflected by her increased succorance and deference scores. In other words, she was much more subtle and indirect in expressing her anger.

C_2 There are many significant changes in this profile. Her drive level increased significantly. She has a much stronger need for achievement, as well as increased need for assuming a supervisory role and handling a position which gives her prestige and status. Much more of her energy appears to be directed in the achievement area. She appears to be much more comfortable in assuming a role which requires her to initiate, advise and direct. Along with this, she appears to be more open, frank, candid, outgoing and self-reliant. Her pre-profile indicates that she was somewhat lacking in self-confidence and tended to be on the self-effacing side. Although she still appears to be self-effacing, this has diminished. It is also noteworthy that her aggressiveness has increased. She is more willing to express her feelings of resentment and anger than she was before; however, her high abasement is probably a restraining influence. It is also significant that her need for working with details and trivia has decreased very significantly. In fact, the post-profile appears to indicate that she has very little concern for minutia to the point that this could be a real problem for her. Thus, she shows definite increase in her achievement motive and her need for self-confidence and assuming a supervisory role, and appears to be more spontaneous and open, less self-effacing, and far less concerned with detail.

D_1 The most significant changes evident in this profile are an increase in drive level or in need for achievement, and also a marked increase in autonomy and need for independence. There is a significant increase in her need to get ahead, to be successful, to accomplish tasks requiring skill and effort, to assume a supervisory role, to persuade and influence others to do what she wants, and to make group decisions. In addition, she has a much stronger need to be independent of others in making decisions, to say what she thinks about things, and to have more independence and autonomy. The post-profile reflects more of an aggressive autonomy. Thus, her level of aggression also increased slightly. It is also interesting that she seems to be much less concerned about details and order, and much more concerned about broader and general aspects. There also appears to be a definite tendency to move away from the pressures of conformity. She is much less deferent and conforming. This goes along with her increased need for independence and autonomy. There also appears to be a significant increase in self-confidence and self-assurance. This is reflected by the fact that her abasement score is much lower. Rather than tending to blame herself for failures, she is more likely to problem-solve in a constructive fashion. In addition to this, she also appears to be slightly more task-oriented and a bit more willing to be noticed in situations. This is reflected by the fact that her nurturance and affiliation scores dropped slightly and her exhibition score went up significantly. To summarize, she showed significant increase in her need for achievement, in independence, in self-confidence and social skills, and a definite tendency on her part to be less concerned with details of a minute and trivial nature and with situations that demand conformity.

D_2 There are a large number of changes in this profile.

The need for influencing others and assuming a supervisory role has increased significantly. She appears to be more comfortable and has a stronger need for assuming positions which require her to advise, initiate, and coordinate. She is also significantly less deferent, and feels much less pressure for conforming and accepting the advice and direction of others. There is a significant increase in her need for being independent. She appears to be much more self-reliant and self-assured. However, there has also been a very large increase in her aggressiveness and her need to be critical, to attack contrary points of view and to become angry, to express her resentment in an open fashion and be argumentative. However, this may be moderated to some degree by the fact that her nurturance has also gone up. Even though she is more aggressive and critical, she is more helpful, giving and warm. There also appears to be a drop in her concern for minor and routine details. She appears to have much more of a generalist point of view.

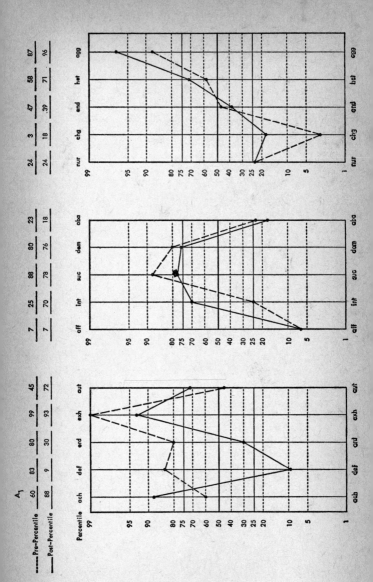

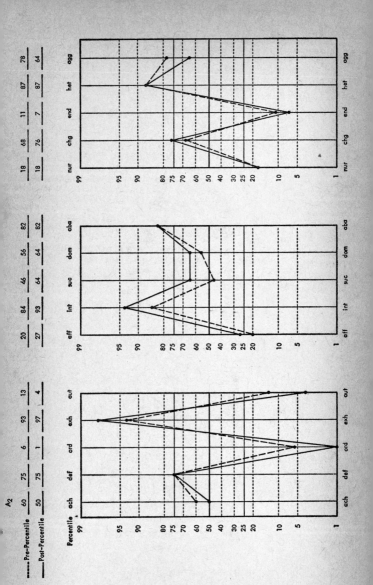

241

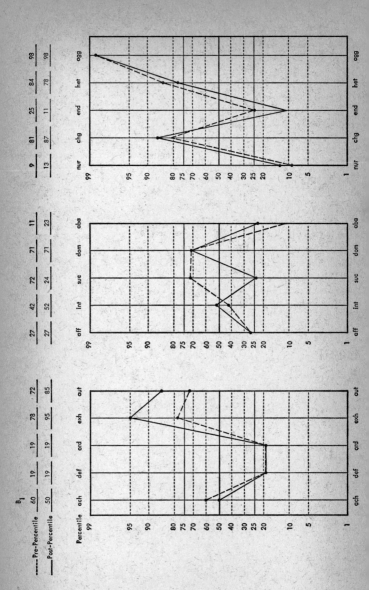

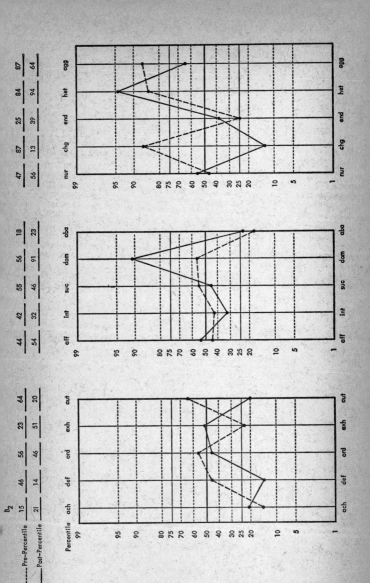

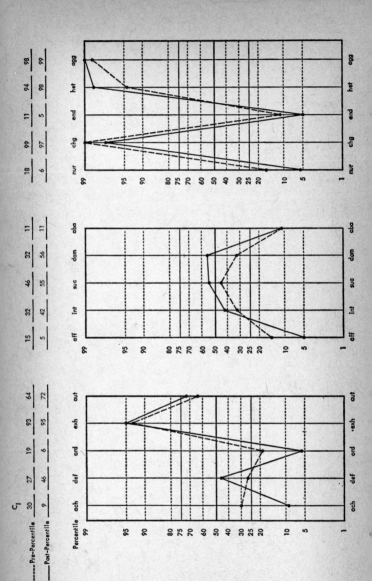

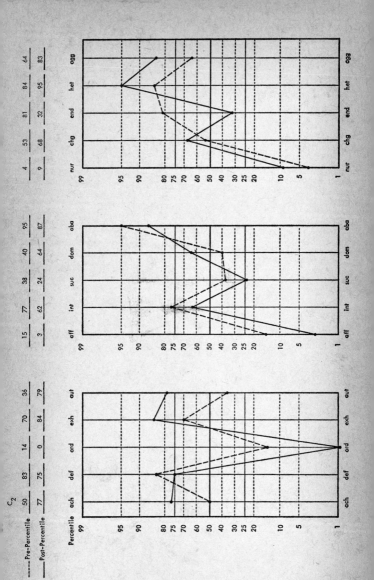

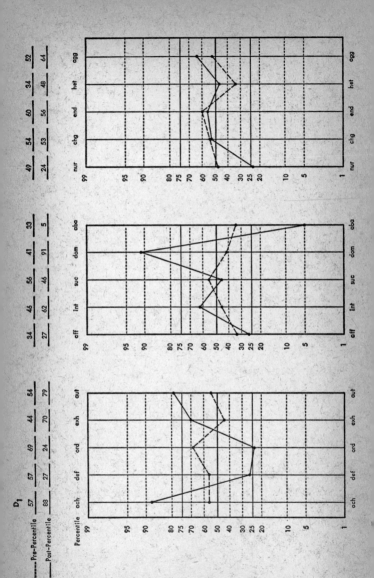

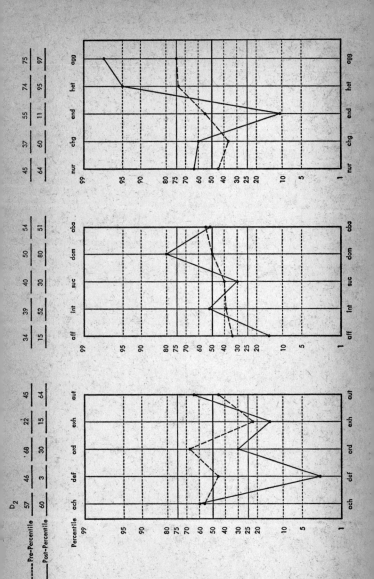

EDWARDS PERSONAL PREFERENCE SCHEDULE PERCENTILES

	A 1 Pre	A 1 Post	A 2 Pre	A 2 Post	B 1 Pre	B 1 Post	B 2 Pre	B 2 Post	C 1 Pre	C 1 Post	C 2 Pre	C 2 Post	D 1 Pre	D 1 Post	D 2 Pre	D 2 Post
Achievement	60	88	60	50	60	50	15	21	30	9	50	77	57	88	57	60
Deference	83	9	75	75	19	19	46	14	27	46	83	75	57	27	46	3
Order	80	30	6	1	19	19	56	46	19	6	14	0	69	24	68	30
Exhibition	99	93	93	97	78	95	23	51	93	95	70	84	44	70	22	15
Autonomy	45	72	13	4	72	85	64	20	64	72	36	79	54	79	45	64
Affiliation	7	7	20	27	27	27	44	54	15	5	15	3	34	27	34	15
Intraception	25	70	84	93	42	52	42	32	32	42	77	62	46	62	39	52
Succorance	88	78	46	64	72	24	55	46	46	55	38	24	56	46	40	30
Dominance	80	76	56	64	71	71	56	91	32	56	40	64	41	91	50	80
Abasement	23	18	82	82	11	23	18	23	11	11	95	87	33	5	54	51
Nurturance	24	24	18	18	9	13	47	56	18	6	4	9	49	24	45	64
Change	3	18	68	76	81	87	87	13	99+	97	53	68	54	53	37	60
Endurance	47	39	11	7	25	11	25	39	11	5	81	32	60	56	55	11
Heterosexuality	58	71	87	87	84	78	84	94	94	98	84	95	34	48	74	95
Aggression	87	96	78	64	98	98	87	64	98	99+	64	83	52	64	75	97
Consistency	66	5	25	25	66	25	25	25	66	45	45	97	45	85	45	25